GLENCOE
HEALTH

Human Sexuality

About the Author:

Mary H. Bronson, Ph.D., has taught health education in grades K–12, as well as health education methods classes at the undergraduate and graduate levels. As health education specialist for the Dallas School District, Dr. Bronson developed and implemented a district-wide health education program, *Skills for Living*, which was used as a model by the state education agency. She has assisted school districts throughout the country in developing local health education programs. She is also the author of Glencoe's *Teen Health* textbook series.

Cover image: McGraw-Hill Education

my.mheducation.com

Send all inquiries to:
McGraw-Hill Education
8787 Orion Place
Columbus, OH 43240

Glencoe Health, Human Sexuality, Teacher Edition:
ISBN: 978-1-26-432024-0
MHID: 1-26-432024-8

Printed in the United States of America.

5 6 7 8 9 10 11 MER 27 26 25 24 23 22

MODULE 1

MODULE 2

MODULE 3

TABLE OF CONTENTS

MODULE 4

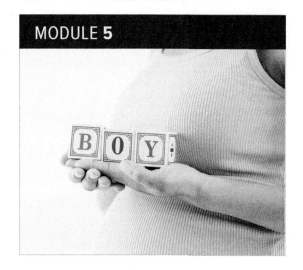

MODULE 5

MODULE 6

MODULE 7

MODULE 8

Glencoe Health Human Sexuality Overview

Although statistics indicate that the number of teens who are sexually active is declining, we need to consider the following:

- The rate of teen pregnancy and births in the United States is among the highest in the Western industrialized world.
- Teens account for approximately one in four new sexually transmitted disease infections annually, about 3.75 million cases each year. Teens and young adults are more likely than other age groups to have multiple sex partners and engage in unprotected sexual activity, putting them at high risk for acquiring most STDs.
- Because HIV can take up to ten years to progress to AIDS, most young adults between the ages of 20 and 29 who have the disease were likely infected as teens. This is nearly one in every five reported AIDS cases.

Glencoe Health Human Sexuality emphasizes using refusal skills, making responsible decisions, and practicing abstinence as ways to help reduce these statistics.

Using *Glencoe Health Human Sexuality*

Most young people have received many messages about sex, but know very little about sexuality. Some teens may have not had opportunities to discuss, in a serious manner, concerns and problems dealing with sexuality or to obtain factual information about it. Nor have they learned or had a chance to apply this practical information while practicing basic life skills, such as decision making, communication, goal setting, refusal, and the application of personal values in life. *Glencoe Health Human Sexuality* presents factual information and encourages students to apply the information when making responsible decisions. There are several points about sexuality education you may wish to keep in mind to use the program successfully.

Parental Involvement

Education about sexuality is a parent's or guardian's right and responsibility. Studies have shown that in homes where there is open communication on sexuality issues, young people tend to follow more traditional norms of sexual behavior. Efforts, thus, should be made to encourage parents or guardians to maintain an open and honest dialogue with their teens on sex-related issues raised in this program.

The most successful efforts in sexuality education are those that result from cooperation between home and school. Parents and guardians should be informed of sexuality programs, have an opportunity to review classroom materials, and, when possible, be provided with materials to use at home.

School and District Policies

Some schools may require parents to sign a letter of permission before their child takes the class. Are there school or state guidelines defining what can and cannot be taught in a class discussing sexuality issues? Find out exactly what the policies are for your school. It may be the case that student response to certain questions may require parental permission. Be aware of any such school and community guidelines before proceeding with this course.

The teacher is the critical key to whether a school-based sexuality program is successful. It is important that you feel comfortable with the subject matter and have a broad base of accurate information. Participating in update workshops as well as a sexuality course can be very helpful. Keep in mind the potential controversy that surrounds any program that includes sexuality topics. By being aware of the feelings and attitudes of the community and knowing how to handle sensitive topics, you may be able to avoid potential problems.

A Word About Refusal Skills

Glencoe Health Human Sexuality reinforces the choice of sexual abstinence for young people and underscores the importance of avoiding all drugs, including alcohol. The choices to abstain from sexual activity before marriage and avoid risk behaviors including alcohol and drug use are viable options for teens. At the same time, and partly because of the role peer pressure and negative media messages play in teens' lives, discussions of and references to these subjects should be presented in a manner that is relevant and has immediacy for them. Telling students to just say no is not enough. Students must be provided with a knowledge base that can influence attitudes and help them choose healthy behaviors. *Glencoe Health Human Sexuality* provides such a motivation, along with the opportunity for students to discuss concerns, learn to deal with and express feelings, and practice communication and assertiveness skills. *Glencoe Health Human Sexuality* encourages students to use a decision-making process to make responsible choices and teaches valuable communication and refusal skills to help them stay out of situations that make them uneasy or that are unhealthy.

Program Components

Glencoe Health Human Sexuality consists of a student text and a Teacher Wraparound Edition. Lesson plans are included to help you teach each lesson and module successfully and efficiently. Answers to Lesson Reviews and Module Assessments are provided at the end of their respective lessons and modules. Helpful teaching tips (indicated by the following headings: **Reading Strategy, Critical Thinking, Universal Access, Health Skills Practice, Writing Support, Cultural Awareness, Active Learning**) are found in the margins of each page. These tips may be used to reinforce and enrich the material found in the lesson.

General Teaching Suggestions

The following are some tips for carrying out the lesson:

- Avoid using the word *you* in teaching (e.g., "When you participate in sexual activity . . ."), which may be construed by students as an advocacy position. Instead, use the third-person pronoun in any class discussion.

- Acknowledge the fact that, historically, sexuality topics have not been discussed openly in our society. As such, some people are likely to be uncomfortable with them and may express this discomfort in any number of inappropriate ways (such as through laughter). Stress the inappropriateness of such responses, underscoring that sexuality is neither a forbidden topic, nor one that should be confined to formal settings (i.e., the classroom).

- Correct the students' use of slang terms (to refer, for example, to parts of the reproductive system) by providing the students with correct terms. This simultaneously creates a trusting and mature environment and encourages free inquiry.

- Avoid asking for personal information or sharing such information about yourself with the class.

- If there are school or state guidelines defining what can and cannot be taught in a class discussing sexuality issues, explain the guidelines to the class. Then, if a question arises that goes beyond the district policy, the students can appreciate why it cannot be addressed in class. Students will support this approach and will not think that you are just dodging a topic.

- Emphasize, especially as you go through the material on teens and high-risk behaviors, that physical and emotional changes occurring during adolescence are normal and vary greatly from person to person. Most students' feelings, thoughts, and concerns are normal.

- Be sure to obtain permission (passive or active) from a parent or guardian prior to teaching about sexuality and/or STDs, as designated by state or local district guidelines. Note that student response to any questions may require prior parental or guardian permission.

- Emphasize mutual respect between students and between teacher and students regarding questions and answers and group participation.
- Encourage students to establish and maintain an open dialogue at home with their parents, guardians, or other adult care providers.

Responding to Student Questions

Here are some suggestions you may wish to follow when responding to student questions:

- All questions should be treated as serious questions. Do not assume that a student's question is being asked to elicit a reaction or get attention. If the question is one that goes beyond school guidelines, explain that fact to students. Advise students to pursue the line of inquiry with parents or in appropriate reference materials.
- Remind students that there is no such thing as a dumb question. Tell students you would rather they ask questions in class, where they can get correct information. Suggest that if they do ask a question, it is likely that others in class have the same question.
- Allow students to submit written questions anonymously if they do not feel comfortable speaking about a topic. Respond to written questions during class.
- Do not allow another student to answer a student's question, which risks not only throwing the discussion off-track, but disseminating incorrect information. If a student asks a question to which you do not know the answer, the appropriate response is to admit not having that information and to assure students that you will find the answer before the next class session. Do not give students the responsibility of hunting for every answer, as this may discourage future open inquiry.
- Repeat any difficult questions to be sure you heard them correctly.
- Answer all questions concisely, but bear in mind that most questions deserve more than a simple yes or no answer. Always take the time to review correct information and make sure students understand.
- Avoid making judgments or imposing your own opinions. This is often done in subtle ways through tone of voice or body language. Be aware of and spend extra time preparing for topics or issues on which you have particularly strong feelings that may be communicated to the class.
- Remember, finally, that new information on topics related to sexuality is being made available on a continual basis, in both the media and professional literature. It is important to stay abreast of current, accurate information from reliable sources and to be prepared to communicate this information to students in a format and style that will reach them.

Use of Resources

Here are some additional suggestions for the introduction and use of outside resource material:

- Any material brought into the classroom should be reviewed thoroughly. Some schools have guidelines concerning what can and cannot be used. Careless dissemination of material can have serious repercussions.
- All audiovisuals should be previewed before being shown. This point is critical. With such delicate subject matter, you will want to be thoroughly familiar with the contents of any video before presenting it.
- All potential guest speakers should be approved by the school administrator before being invited. You should discuss guidelines with the speaker prior to the presentation. In addition, the speaker should be advised of the main objectives of the course and the specific lesson.

Additional Resources

Information on topics related to sexuality is always changing, particularly in the area of sexually transmitted diseases and HIV/AIDS. The following table provides current information you may choose to use as part of your health class discussion. This table gives a synopsis of common STDs. This information corresponds with that in the *Sexually Transmitted Diseases* Module of the student text. The chart includes a description of the STD, its cause, symptoms (when present), and treatment. It is important to remind students that in many cases, symptoms of STDs are not obvious.

Sexually Transmitted Diseases

Disease	Description	Cause	Symptoms	Treatment
Chlamydia	An infection that attacks the male and female reproductive organs	The bacterium *Chlamydia trachomatis*	Females—(early) abnormal vaginal discharge, burning during urination; (late) pelvic inflammatory disease (PID), which involves severe pelvic pain, infertility, increased chance of ectopic pregnancy Males—(early) discharge from the penis, burning during urination; (late) damage to reproductive organs	Antibiotics
Gonorrhea	A disease that attacks the mucous membranes of the penis, vagina, uterus, rectum, and throat	The bacterium *Neisseria gonorrhoeae*	Females—(early) yellow vaginal discharge, burning during urination; (late) PID Males—(early) yellow-whitish discharge from the penis, burning during urination, painful or swollen testes; (late) epididymitis, infertility Both—(late) life-threatening infection of blood or joints	Antibiotics
Human Papillomavirus (HPV)	A virus that can cause genital warts, asymptomatic infection, and cancer	Human papillomavirus (HPV)	Soft, moist, pink or red swellings, often in clusters on the genitals, anus, groin, or thigh; often asymptomatic	No cure; removal of warts by laser or by freezing, burning, cutting; injected antiviral drug; topical ointments
Genital Herpes	Blisters in the genital or rectal area	Herpes simplex virus type 2 (HSV-2)	Blisters within two weeks of contact; fever; swollen glands	No cure; antiviral drugs reduce duration and severity of episodes
Hepatitis B	A disease that attacks the liver	Hepatitis B virus (HBV)	Jaundice, fatigue, abdominal pain, nausea and vomiting, joint pain, loss of appetite	Drugs that are effective in about 40 percent of patients
Hepatitis C	A disease that causes liver damage	Hepatitis C virus (HCV)	Often asymptomatic; jaundice, fatigue, abdominal pain, loss of appetite, nausea and vomiting	Antiviral drugs, combination treatments effective in 40 to 80 percent of cases depending on type

Sexually Transmitted Diseases (continued)

Disease	Description	Cause	Symptoms	Treatment
Syphilis	A progressive disease that affects the entire body if left untreated	The bacterium *Treponema pallidum*	*Primary stage*—chancre, a painless sore *Secondary stage*—infectious rash on palms of hands and soles of feet; flu-like symptoms, hair loss, weight loss *Late syphilis*—symptoms disappear during latent period; then slow, progressive loss of muscular coordination, paralysis, blindness, dementia, sometimes death	Antibiotics cure disease but cannot repair damage already done
Trichomoniasis and Bacterial Vaginosis	Vaginitis, or inflammation of the vagina; infection of the urethra in males (Trichomoniasis only)	The protozoan parasite *Trichomonas vaginalis* and an imbalance of bacteria normally found in the vagina, respectively	Females—odorous vaginal discharge, genital irritation, itching, discomfort Males—mild discharge from penis, irritation, burning (Trichomoniasis only)	Prescription drug metronidazole (for both)
Pubic Lice	Tiny parasitic insects that live in pubic hair and sometimes in coarse hair of legs, armpits, mustaches, beards, eyebrows, eyelashes	The parasitic insect *Phthirus pubis*	Intense itching in the genital area and/or other areas of infestation	Special medicated shampoo for pubic hair and hair of legs, armpits, mustaches, beards; special prescription ointment for eyebrows, eyelashes
Scabies	Microscopic mites that burrow into the skin	The parasitic mite *Sarcoptes scabiei*	Pimplelike rash with severe itching in the genital area and/ or other areas of infestation 4–6 weeks after contact	Medicated lotions; additional medications for itching

MODULE 1 | Sexuality and You

MODULE 1	STANDARDS / NOTES	LESSON ASSESSMENT
	Use this space for standards and notes.	Module 1 Assessment Online assessment
LESSON 1 **Sexuality and Making Responsible Decisions** **BIG IDEA.** You will experience many changes in your physical, mental/emotional, and social health during adolescence. *30 MIN.*		Lesson 1 Review Online assessment
LESSON 2 **Adolescence and Development** **BIG IDEA.** Accomplishing certain developmental tasks and responsibilities can help teens in the process of achieving adulthood. *30 MIN.*		Lesson 2 Review Online assessment
LESSON 3 **Adolescence—A Time of Change** **BIG IDEA.** Hormones will cause many physical changes to your body as you experience puberty. *30 MIN.*		Lesson 3 Review Online assessment

Key to Abilities   Teaching Strategies and Activities have been coded for ability level and appropriateness.

AL Activities for students working above grade level

BL Activities for students working below grade level

OL Activities for students working on grade level

EL Activities for English Learners

Sexuality and You

Module Overview Module 1 focuses on the physical, mental/emotional, and social changes that begin to occur during the teen years and responsible strategies for communicating wants and needs.

LESSON 1
Identify the physical, mental/emotional, and social changes that occur during adolescence.

LESSON 2
Identify the developmental tasks of adolescence and demonstrate strategies for communicating needs, wants, and emotions that lead to responsible behaviors.

LESSON 3
Identify the causes of the physical changes that occur during adolescence and relate the development of secondary sex characteristics to chemical changes that occur within the body.

Activating Prior Knowledge

Using Visuals Have students look at the picture on this page. Explain that during adolescence, a person's sense of masculinity or femininity develops and matures.

Ask Students: *In what ways does this process affect a teen's self-image?*

Sexuality and Making Responsible Decisions

FOCUS

BIG IDEA You will experience many changes in your physical, mental/emotional, and social health during adolescence.

Allow students to describe the products that use sexual messages in their advertisements. Then discuss why so many advertisers use these types of messages to sell their products. **Sample answer: People want to identify with the people in the ad; sexual messages catch attention.**

Reading Strategy

Predict Students' questions will vary.

QUICKWRITE

Before students answer, write down the following on the board for students to answer: *What kinds of product advertisements in magazines or television commercials promote products by using sexual messages?* **Accept reasonable responses.**

Student Objectives

- Explain how sexuality develops.
- Identify the physical, mental/emotional, and social changes that occur during adolescence.
- Identify decision-making skills that promote individual, family, and community health.
- Summarize the advantages of seeking advice and feedback when making healthful decisions.

TEACH

Critical Thinking

Discuss Ask students to talk about some of the pressures, in addition to the media, that teens may experience when making decisions about sexuality issues. OL

Sexuality and Making Responsible Decisions

BEFORE YOU READ

Predict. Scan the headings, subheadings, and photo captions in this lesson. Write a list of questions that you have about sexuality.

Vocabulary
sexuality
self-concept
goal

BIG IDEA You will experience many changes in your physical, mental/emotional, and social health during adolescence.

QUICK WRITE

People make decisions every day that affect their health. *Write a paragraph describing a decision that you recently made concerning your physical, mental/emotional, or social health.*

Questions About Sexuality

A common theme in books, magazines, movies, and on the Internet is the use of sexual messages. Advertisers often try to use sexual messages to help them sell their products. These media messages can impact a teen's views on sexual activity. Studies suggest that teens who are exposed to high levels of sexual material on television are more likely to engage in sexual activity themselves. With that in mind, consider the following:

- Sixty-four percent of TV shows display some form of sexual content.
- Only 15 percent of these TV shows address risks associated with sexual activity or present abstinence as an alternative.

Even though information on and promotion of sex seem to be everywhere, some people feel uncomfortable with the way that sexuality is openly presented. To them, sex is a private matter, and they don't talk about it or ask questions about it.

How do people know they have all the facts? It's important to have factual information about sexuality issues to help you understand your growth and development. This course will address some important issues about sexuality and help you make responsible decisions that protect your health and prevent diseases.

Sexuality and Health

Your **sexuality** refers to everything about the characteristics of your gender. It includes the way you act, your personality, and how you feel about yourself. Learning about sexuality is an ongoing process. It changes as you live, grow, and develop. Your sexuality is an integral part of your health and well-being, including your physical, mental/emotional, and social health.

Physical Health

Good physical health means that you have enough energy to perform the activities of daily life and to cope with everyday stresses and challenges. When you are in good physical health, your body can resist infections and you are more able to protect yourself from injury. Being physically healthy involves:

- Getting at least eight hours of sleep each night.
- Eating nutritious meals.
- Being physically active on a regular basis.
- Drinking up to eight 8-ounce glasses of water each day.
- Avoiding harmful substances, such as tobacco, alcohol, and other drugs.

It is equally important to take care of your reproductive system by practicing healthful behaviors. Practice good hygiene, get regular physical exams, and make responsible decisions that protect against unplanned pregnancy and sexually transmitted diseases.

Regular physical activity is one of the keys to good physical health. **What physical activities do you enjoy?**

Mental and Emotional Health

Mental and emotional health refers to how well you adjust and adapt to your surroundings. People with good mental health:

- Generally feel good about themselves and tend to be self-confident.
- Relate well to other people and are able to cope with life's daily demands.
- Understand their feelings and express themselves in considerate and appropriate ways.
- Use reason and have developed emotional maturity and critical-thinking skills.

A strong relationship exists between good mental health and a good **self-concept**. This is the mental image you have about yourself. It is your unique set of perceptions, ideas, and attitudes about yourself. From the time you are an infant, you receive a variety of signals from people around you that influence how you see yourself. Self-concept is probably the single most important factor influencing what you do. It influences your ability to make healthful choices. People who respect themselves are more likely to take better care of themselves than people with low self-concepts.

Photodisc/Getty Images

Sexuality and Making Responsible Decisions **3**

Sexuality and Making Responsible Decisions

Critical Thinking

Class Discussion Ask students whether they think popular entertainment—movies, television, and music—glamorize sex. Discuss how they feel they are influenced by these sources. Then ask students to provide examples of songs, movies, or television shows that deal with the risks of sexual intercourse, such as unplanned pregnancy and sexually transmitted diseases. Have students discuss the frequency of these examples compared to the examples of sex being glamorized. OL

Reading Strategy

Building Vocabulary Have students look up the vocabulary words *self-concept* and *goal* in the Glossary/Glosario. Have them infer ways the two terms relate. OL BL EL

Critical Thinking

Peer Pressure Have students discuss the ways they have learned about sexuality. These could include a discussion with parents or information learned from a book. Record this list on the board. Point out that many of our decisions are influenced by peer pressure and that often this pressure is negative—that others try to convince us to do something unwise, unhealthy, or wrong. OL

Caption Answer: *Answers will vary.*

LESSON 1
Sexuality and Making Responsible Decisions

Critical Thinking

Responsible Decisions Have students consider the relationship between avoiding alcohol and other drugs, and making responsible decisions that protect against unplanned pregnancy and sexually transmitted diseases. OL

Class Discussion Put the following headings on the board: *Physical, Mental/Emotional,* and *Social.* Brainstorm and list ways to promote healthy sexuality in each area. OL

Reading Strategy

Emphasize Point out that the values and beliefs of a person's family or other adult caregivers form the basis for that individual's personal value system and standards of behavior. OL

Active Learning

Class Activity Have students discuss the relationship between one's mental health and his or her self-concept. Ask students to create a list of people who influence a person's self-concept. Then discuss how positive role models can affect one's physical health. OL

Caption Answer: *Learning to communicate well, expressing yourself, and being able to handle sexual feelings responsibly.*

A person with a good self-concept is less likely to seek love and approval by becoming involved in high-risk behaviors, such as engaging in sexual activity, or using alcohol, tobacco, and other drugs. Learning to communicate well and to express, understand, and responsibly manage sexual feelings enhances self-concept along with mental and emotional health.

Social Health
Adolescence is a time of tremendous change, not only for your body, mind, and emotions, but also for your relationships. During this period, you often begin to examine your values and beliefs as well as those of your family. You may compare them to those of friends and society at large. You may start working to shape your own values and standards of behavior into a personal value system that is your own. As you mature, you can benefit from seeking advice and feedback from parents or trusted adults to help you make healthful decisions. This process helps you begin to build your independent identity for the adult world.

Making Responsible Decisions

As a teen, you are faced with choices that can have either positive or negative effects on your overall health. The decisions you make in some of these situations can affect your life and perhaps the life of your peers for years to come. It is important to know how to decide what to do and consider the consequences to the health and safety of you and your peers.

The messages you receive from others help form your self-concept, the mental image you have of yourself. **What other factors help you to live a healthy life?**

Decisions, especially about your health and sexuality, can be difficult to make. When you are confronted with a difficult decision, it helps to break the decision down into smaller, more manageable steps. This decision-making model can help you act in ways that promote your health, self-esteem, and respect for others. Decision-making requires six basic steps.

1. **State the situation.** Be sure you understand the situation. Ask yourself what is involved, how did the problem develop, and how much time do you have to make a decision?
2. **List the options.** Think of as many ways of solving the problem as you can. Enlist the help of parents, teachers, or trusted friends to get other ideas.
3. **Weigh the possible outcomes.** Consider the consequences of each option, using the word HELP as a guide:

   • **H** (Healthful) What health risks, if any, will this option present?
   • **E** (Ethical) Does this choice reflect what you believe is right or wrong?
   • **L** (Legal) Does it violate any local, state, or federal laws?
   • **P** (Parental approval) Would your parents or guardians approve of this choice?

4. **Consider values.** Values are the ideas, beliefs, and attitudes about what is important that help guide the way you live. Consider how each option will reflect your values.
5. **Make a decision and act on it.** Put together all the information you have, make a responsible decision, and act.
6. **Evaluate the decision.** After you have made the decision and taken action, examine the consequences of your decision. How did your decision affect your health and the health of others? Were there any unintended consequences? What did you learn that you would apply in the future?

Goal Setting and Health Decisions

A **goal** is something you aim for that takes planning and work. Goal setting involves making decisions that will help you meet a goal you have set for yourself. How successfully you meet your goals depends on the decisions you make now.

Time is a consideration when you are setting goals. A short-term goal, such as completing a class project, is something you can complete in a short amount of time. A long-term goal is a goal you would reach in a longer amount of time.

You will often be faced with difficult decisions. What are the six steps to follow in the decision-making process?

LESSON 1
Sexuality and Making Responsible Decisions

Health Skills Practice

Practicing Healthful Behaviors Take the time to practice the decision-making process. Use a sample student problem and have the class work through each step. It is critical that students practice identifying all possible options and evaluating the consequences of each. OL

Active Learning

Class Activity Ask each student to write down the names of three people he or she could talk to regarding an important decision about sexual activity. Tell students to keep this paper for future reference. OL

Gender-Role Stereotypes Divide the class into females and males. Have each group compile a list of famous people (entertainers, politicians, businesspeople) who they consider to be typically "feminine" or "masculine." Have students list the characteristics that led to their choices. Use the lists to begin a discussion of how gender-role stereotypes are reinforced. OL

Cooperative Learning

Decision-Making Model Divide the class into four groups. Have each group work through the following problem using the decision-making model: One day while walking to school, one of three friends suggests skipping school and going to the local mall. Instruct the groups to begin by stating the situation that requires a decision and listing all of the possible options. Encourage them to be as thorough as they can. When discussing the group responses with the class, stress the role peer pressure might play in such a decision. AL

Caption Answer: *State the situation, list the options, weigh the outcomes, consider values, make a decision and act on it, and evaluate the decision.*

Sexuality and Making Responsible Decisions

Critical Thinking

Positive Goals Ask students to give examples of situations in which they want to set goals for themselves (for example, going to college, completing a difficult course, doing well on a sports team). Have students identify someone who could help them achieve their goals. OL

Health Skills Practice

Goal Setting Divide the class into four groups. Have each group choose a goal that a teen might set regarding dating. Then have students work through the goal-setting process. Evaluate the steps students have decided on and discuss the effects that both positive and negative peer pressure might have on such a goal. AL

ASSESS

Progress Monitoring

Reteaching Have students review the six goal-setting steps. Encourage them to explain in their own words how they would set about accomplishing a specific goal. Explain that the goal-setting steps can be used to reach both simple and complex goals.

Enrichment

- Have students write a paragraph about how the influences on their social health change during adolescence.
- Have students write a paragraph about how using the decision-making process can help with important decisions.

Sum up the lesson by reminding students that adolescence is a time of tremendous change, and that they can make many important decisions that will promote their physical, mental/emotional, and social health. Remind students to talk to a trusted adult about any questions that were not answered in this lesson.

Caption Answer: *Possible answers: select a goal and write it down; list the steps you will take to reach your goal; identify sources of help and support; set a reasonable time frame for reaching your goal; evaluate your progress by establishing checkpoints; reward yourself after achieving your goal.*

Health Minute

These are strategies for meeting emotional needs in healthy ways:

- Focus on recognizing the things you do well and be willing to improve on areas that can use some attention and effort.
- Pay attention to your feelings and listen to your body.
- Discover interests beyond your school day by getting involved in after-school activities.
- Reach out to help people in need in your community, such as older adults, children, and individuals who need assistance.

Short-term goals can also be steps in completing a long-term goal. For example, Ava and Mike have been dating for a while and they are talking about having sex. Ava wants to feel closer to her boyfriend, but she also has long-term goals of going to college and starting a career. She decides that practicing abstinence now will help her reach her long-term goal.

- **Select a goal and write it down.** Make it specific, realistic, and something that is important to you and your health.
- **List the steps you will take to reach your goal.** Break your goal into smaller, short-term goals.
- **Identify sources of help and support.** Sources might include parents or guardians, other family members, friends, peers, or teachers.
- **Set a reasonable time frame for reaching your goal.** After deciding on a reasonable time, put it in writing.
- **Evaluate your progress by establishing checkpoints.** Periodically check your progress and make any necessary adjustments that will help you reach your goal.
- **Reward yourself after achieving your goal.** Choose a reward that is attainable and healthful.

Goals can be short-term, such as giving a class presentation, or long-term, such as what kind of career you would like to have. **What steps can you take to help you set and achieve your goals?**

Steve Debenport/E+/Getty Images

Lesson 1 Review

Facts and Vocabulary

1. Define *sexuality* and discuss how it develops.
2. Identify three areas of health that are affected by changes during adolescence.
3. Define *self-concept* and explain what influences a teen's self-concept.
4. How can you apply the decision-making process to make responsible decisions?

Thinking Critically

5. **Synthesize.** Make a list of positive mental and emotional changes that occur during adolescence. Describe two specific skills you can develop to promote good physical, mental, and emotional health for yourself, your family, and your community.
6. **Analyze.** Summarize the advantages of seeking advice and feedback when making healthful decisions. How can a positive self-concept affect decision making? Give two examples.

Applying Health Skills

7. **Goal Setting.** Think about an important goal that you would like to achieve that is related to an extracurricular activity. Use the goal-setting process to map out an action plan for working toward your goal. Which decisions were the easiest to make? Which ones were the most difficult?

6 Sexuality and You

Lesson 1 Review Answers

1. Sexuality is everything about you as a male or female. Your sexuality develops over time as you live, grow, and develop.
2. The three aspects are physical health, mental/emotional health, and social health.
3. Self-concept is the mental image you have about yourself. It develops over time, beginning in infancy, from the variety of signals you get from people around you.
4. Break the decision-making process down into small steps, such as the six basic steps.
5. Answers will vary but should include aspects of physical growth and development and mental/emotional maturity, as well as basic physical and mental/emotional self-care discussed in the lesson.
6. Answers will vary but should demonstrate the student understands that a healthy self-concept promotes healthy, self-protective behavior, and a low self-concept makes self-destructive behavior more likely.
7. Action plans will vary but should include the first four steps of the goal-setting process.

Adolescence and Development

BIG IDEA Accomplishing certain developmental tasks and responsibilities can help teens in the process of achieving adulthood.

QUICK WRITE

Fold a piece of paper evenly into thirds to make three vertical columns. Label the columns "Physical," "Mental/Emotional," and "Social." Under each heading, write how you have changed since childhood in that category. *Write as many specific examples as you can.*

Tasks of Adolescence

During adolescence, many physical, mental/emotional, and social changes take place in the human body. As an adolescent, you also experience more subtle cognitive changes. These can cause you to approach problems in new ways. Everyone goes through this in the process of achieving adulthood. **Cognitive** changes are those relating to the ability to reason and think out abstract solutions.

Based on the work of sociologist Robert Havighurst, adolescents must accomplish certain milestones during their teens and into their twenties. These milestones are called **developmental tasks**. A developmental task is an event that needs to occur during a particular age period for a person to continue his or her growth toward becoming a healthy, mature adult. These tasks are summarized below:

- Adjusting to and accepting a new physical sense of self
- Adjusting to new intellectual abilities and new cognitive demands at school
- Developing expanded verbal skills to allow for expression of more complex concepts and needs
- Achieving and managing a masculine or feminine social role and a personal sense of identity
- Establishing adult goals of marriage and/or career
- Establishing emotional and psychological independence from parents
- Forming more mature and stable relationships with peers
- Adopting a personal value system and standards of behavior
- Developing a behavioral maturity

BEFORE YOU READ

Explain. Write the Vocabulary terms in your notebook and add a definition written in your own words. After reading the lesson, check your definitions against those in the glossary.

Vocabulary
cognitive
developmental tasks
empathy

Adolescence and Development **7**

FOCUS

BIG IDEA Accomplishing certain developmental tasks and responsibilities can help teens in the process of achieving adulthood.

As a person moves from childhood to adolescence, his or her ability to handle difficult situations increases as he or she becomes more emotionally and intellectually mature. Tell students that in this lesson they will learn about tasks they need to accomplish before being ready to assume the responsibilities of adulthood.

Reading Strategy

Explain Students should create entries for the new vocabulary terms, using definitions based on their current knowledge.

QUICKWRITE

Before students answer, write the following on the board for students to answer: *How does a child react to a difficult situation? How would you react to a difficult situation? Would an adult react differently?* **Accept reasonable responses.**

Student Objectives:

- Identify the developmental tasks of adolescence.
- Demonstrate strategies for communicating needs, wants, and emotions that lead to responsible behaviors.
- Analyze how changes during adolescence lead to an increased ability to have respect and empathy for other people.

TEACH

Critical Thinking

Gender Roles Examine some male and female roles depicted on TV shows. Ask students to spot ways in which these roles are stereotypes and to determine the effect such stereotyping has on their personal identities and their ability to achieve a healthy self-concept. OL

Reading Strategy

Building Vocabulary Tell students that the word development comes from the Old French word *developer,* which means "to unwrap" or "to expose." Have students look up the meaning of the suffix –al ("relating to or characterized by") and use the meanings of the Old French word and the suffix to determine what the phrase *developmental tasks* might mean. OL BL **EL**

LESSON 2
Adolescence and Development

Active Learning

Developing Skills Ask students to name skills they think an adult should have. List the responses on the board. Skills listed might include such things as filling out income tax forms or planning a family budget. After you have seven or eight skills listed, have students pick one skill and show how it relates to at least one of the developmental tasks. OL

Critical Thinking

Responsible Decisions Ask students to explain how succeeding at each of the developmental tasks contributes to a person's ability to make responsible decisions. For example, developing behavioral maturity leads to behaving in a responsible manner, which is a result of making responsible decisions. OL

Reading Strategies

Emphasize Help students make the connection between higher-level thinking skills and their ability to care for others. When you allow another person to express thoughts or ideas that you don't agree with or that may be new to you, you show you care about that person and that you can implement higher-level thinking. OL

Cooperative Learning

Developmental Tasks Divide the class into nine groups. Assign each group one of the developmental tasks listed in the lesson. Have each group develop a list of actions that would help an adolescent achieve that task. For example, one group may suggest that an adolescent could study vocabulary words for the SAT, which would expand his or her verbal skills. Groups should share their lists with the rest of the class. AL

Caption Answer: *Your verbal skills help to communicate logical, abstract thinking, such as considering others' points of view.*

Intellectual Development

Until about the age of 12, children think in "concrete" terms, and they believe only what they can see. Consider the following experiment:

Show a child two containers that hold exactly the same volume of water but are shaped differently: one container is tall and thin, the other short and wide. Pour the same amount of water into each container. The child is likely to say that there is more water in the taller container.

This experiment demonstrates the concrete thinking of the child. As an adolescent, you have bridged that gap between concrete and abstract thought, and now you are capable of more complex thinking:

- **Abstract thinking.** Abstract thinking allows you to analyze and evaluate information, to better understand cause and effect, to examine consequences, and to draw your own conclusions.

- **Logical thinking.** Along with abstract thinking comes growth in mental abilities and an ability to use logic to reason things out. In your head, you can go through the steps from point A to point B and figure out possible consequences.

- **Other, higher-level thinking.** Your ability to see the finer points of an issue increase, and you are also able to remember more. You may find that you are more willing to consider points of view other than your own.

Your ability to think on a higher level increases in adolescence. **How have your verbal skills helped you to show maturity?**

8 Sexuality and You

Developing Responsibility

During adolescence, it is natural to work toward achieving independence from your parents or guardians. Teens develop independence in many ways, including the following:

- Taking on a part-time job
- Establishing new goals
- Developing personal values
- Exploring new interests
- Spending more time with friends
- Dating

As this process occurs, you will make more decisions on your own. Being responsible means you accept the results that come with those decisions. In creating rules and limits, parents teach teens responsibility and consequences. As teens grow closer to adulthood, parents will allow them to make increasingly complex decisions. With each new choice, you become more confident in your decision-making skills. As you make more and more decisions, it is important to remember that you are the one responsible for your choices and that the consequences that follow are your responsibility as well.

The ability to express yourself in mature ways will allow you to make responsible decisions in any relationship. **What is one way to develop independence?**

Eric Audras/Onoky/SuperStock

Adolescence and Development **9**

Health Skills Activity

Decision Making After students have read the scenario, guide them through each step of the decision-making process. Have groups plan and present role-plays to demonstrate a health-enhancing decision Paul can make. OL

Writing Support

Research Have students find articles and other sources of information about artificial intelligence. Ask them to write a short essay about the cognitive abilities of which computers are not yet capable. AL

Caption Answer: *Possible answers: Taking on a part-time job, establishing new goals, or developing personal values.*

Adolescence and Development

Critical Thinking

Empathy Ask students to suggest situations in which feeling empathy for a peer might help that person. (For example, if you feel empathy for a classmate who has done poorly on a test, your empathy might lead you to suggest a study session in which you help the other student.) OL

ASSESS

Reteaching Have students review the list of developmental tasks from the lesson and explain in their own words what each task involves. Explain to them that just as toddlers need to learn certain tasks to progress to the next stage of childhood, they as adolescents need to accomplish these tasks to grow into capable, mature adults.

Enrichment To compare the reasoning abilities of people at different ages, have students develop a simple problem: Your friends come by and want you to go to a movie with them. You haven't finished your chores/homework/work. What should you do? Why? Have students ask a 10-year-old, a 12-year-old, a 15-year-old, a 20-year-old, and a 30-year-old how each would solve the problem. Then have students compare the answers and discuss possible reasons for the difference they discover.

Sum up the lesson by reminding students that adolescence is a time of many changes. In fact, during adolescence, individuals experience the greatest degree of change than in any period of life.

Character Check

You can demonstrate caring by considering the feelings of others and by showing kindness toward people around you. Make a list of other ways to show you care about friends and family members.

Developing Mature Relationships

One part of a teen's social development is a growing ability to feel more deeply and consider the needs of other people. This process is crucial to forming more mature peer relationships. As children, most people learn **empathy.** Empathy is the ability to feel what others feel, and to put yourself in someone else's place. As an adolescent, you are developing more sensitivity toward others that goes beyond a child's ability to cry when another cries. Your thinking skills allow you to understand the feelings of a friend, and motivate you to want to help your friend resolve whatever it is that is causing distress.

When you demonstrate empathy toward others and offer help, you must always remember to show respect for the other person's feelings, goals, and ideas. Even if you do not share the person's feelings, you can show that you care. Always remember, too, that good friends never urge each other to do something that goes against their beliefs.

Your ability to communicate and express yourself in mature ways will allow you to make responsible decisions in any relationship. When you know how to communicate your feelings, you will be better equipped to avoid unhealthful risk behaviors.

Lesson 2 Review

Facts and Vocabulary

1. Define *developmental task*.

2. Name four of the developmental tasks for adolescents suggested by sociologist Robert Havighurst.

3. What process is crucial to forming more mature peer relationships and the ability to demonstrate empathy?

Thinking Critically

4. **Evaluate.** Review the list of Robert Havighurst's developmental tasks. Which ones do you think would be the most difficult to attain? Explain your reasoning.

5. **Analyze.** Explain how changes that occur during adolescence lead to increased cognitive abilities and the ability to communicate needs, wants, and emotions. Provide two examples of ways that a teen might show that she is developing more complex thinking abilities.

Applying Health Skills

6. **Communication Skills.** Write a dialogue in which a teen offers assistance and empathy to a friend who is having a problem. Show how the teen demonstrates empathy and communicates consideration in a respectful way.

10 Sexuality and You

Lesson 2 Review Answers

1. A developmental task is something that needs to occur during a particular age period for a person to continue his or her growth toward maturity.
2. Answers will vary but should include four of the nine tasks outlined in the lesson.
3. The process of thinking and caring about other people is crucial to forming more mature relationships.
4. Answers will vary, but students should support their choices with clear reasoning.
5. Answers should reflect an understanding of the shift from concrete to abstract thinking, the ability to think logically, and the ability to appreciate finer points of an issue as well as others' views. Examples should demonstrate use of at least two of these higher-level thinking skills.
6. Dialogues will vary, but one or more of the characters represented should be shown to behave responsibly, showing respect and empathy toward other characters.

Adolescence—A Time of Change

BIG IDEA Hormones will cause many physical changes to your body as you experience puberty.

QUICK WRITE

Suppose you have a younger sister or brother age 10 or 11 who is the same gender as you. If your sister or brother asked you what changes they should expect to go through during the next few years, what would you say? *Write your answer and be as specific as possible. Include emotional as well as physical changes.*

Puberty

The body is remarkably complex. Its organ systems work together to create and regulate growth, change, flexibility, and stability. The nervous system is the primary regulating system of the body; it works closely with the **endocrine system** to regulate a variety of body functions. The endocrine system is a body system made up of ductless glands that secrete chemicals called hormones into the blood. Hormones are chemical substances produced in glands, which regulate the activities of different body cells and organs. Hormones control the changes that occur during puberty.

During adolescence, hormones signal your body to make the changes that occur during **puberty**. Puberty is the period of growth from physical childhood to physical adulthood, when a person develops certain traits of his or her own gender. Puberty is marked by periods of rapid, uneven physical growth, and all teens go through it at their own pace. Changes during puberty occur at different times for each individual. The variation in sizes and shapes among people the same age is entirely normal. These changes typically occur between ages 12 and 18. Puberty includes maturing mentally and affects how teens view themselves and others. In addition to body changes, teens also experience emotional changes brought on by the increase in hormones.

BEFORE YOU READ

Explain. Write a paragraph describing why adolescence is a time of change. What types of physical, mental/emotional, and social changes do adolescents experience?

Vocabulary
endocrine system
puberty
pituitary gland

Adolescence—A Time of Change

FOCUS

BIG IDEA Hormones will cause many physical changes to your body as you experience puberty.

Introduce the lesson by stating that during adolescence, individuals go through puberty. During puberty, hormones released by the pituitary gland and the gonads cause adolescents to grow and to develop secondary sex characteristics.

Reading Strategy

Explain Students' answers will vary.

QUICKWRITE

Before students answer, write the following on the board for students to answer. *What are some of the physical changes that take place during adolescence?* **Accept reasonable responses.**

Student Objectives:

- Identify the causes of physical changes that occur during adolescence.
- Explain the role of hormones during puberty.
- Relate the development of secondary sex characteristics to chemical changes that occur within the body.

TEACH

Active Learning

Graphs Ask student to write down their height and gender on a piece of paper. Collect the papers and have students assist in creating a double bar graph or separate bar graphs for each gender. Explain that the second-fastest growth period of one's life occurs during puberty, when growth can be very uneven and can vary greatly from person-to-person. At no other time in our lives is there such a difference in the sizes and shapes of people who are the same age. OL

Reading Strategy

Building Vocabulary *Endo-* means "within;" *exo-* means "out." Exocrine glands in the body—tear and oil glands for example—secrete chemicals into ducts that deliver the chemicals to a specific organ or location. Endocrine glands do not have ducts, but release their chemicals directly into the blood. Ask students to name some of the endocrine glands and the chemicals they secrete. OL

Adolescence—A Time of Change

Reading Strategy

Emphasize Help students to understand that neither the release of hormones by the endocrine system nor the action of such hormones on the body is under conscious control. This principle applies equally to glands involved with digestion and those involved with sexual maturation. OL

Active Learning

Interview Have students interview one parent or guardian, using the following list of questions: What were the main concerns you had as a teen? What did your parents say about your choice of friends? In what kinds of social activities did you participate? Do not ask students to share the information they learned. Instead, conduct a class discussion about the overall interview experience. Ask students if the interviews made them feel any closer to their parents or guardians. Did they find out that the adult shared some of the same feelings they are now experiencing? Help students realize that their parents or guardians, like all adults, went through changes during puberty and experienced the concerns and problems of adolescence. OL

Reading Strategy

Building Vocabulary Have students look up the words *hormones* and *pituitary gland* in the Glossary/Glosario. Then draw the following diagram for the class:

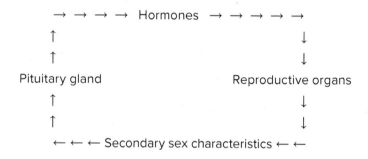

Beginning with "pituitary gland" and moving clockwise, help students explore the relationship illustrated: During adolescence, the pituitary gland releases hormones that stimulate the body to grow. Two of those hormones cause the reproductive organs to produce hormones of their own that cause the development of secondary sex characteristics. Have students suggest other words that might be added and branched out from the map. AL **EL**

Caption Answer: *hormones*

Hormones and the Pituitary Gland

Hormones act as chemical stimulators that regulate body functions in three ways:

- **Hormones stimulate reactions in parts of the body.** For example, in an emergency situation; your heart races, your mouth gets dry, and your palms sweat. You cannot control the secretion of a hormone or your body's reaction to it. Keep this in mind as you learn about other hormonal effects.

- **Hormones produce structural changes in the body during growth periods.** Changes include bone development, maturation of reproductive organs, and development of secondary sex characteristics.

- **Hormones regulate the rate of metabolism.** This is the rate at which body cells produce energy.

The hormones responsible for changes in your body during puberty are released by the **pituitary gland**. The pituitary gland is the gland that controls much of the endocrine system. It releases hormones that affect the brain, glands, skin, bones, muscles, and reproductive organs. It is about the size of a pea and is located at the base of the brain. An area of the brain called the hypothalamus stimulates the pituitary gland to release the necessary hormones. The pituitary gland also secretes two hormones that are responsible for stimulating maturation of the reproductive organs that produce sex cells. These organs are the testes in the male and the ovaries in the female. The two hormones are LH (luteinizing hormone) and FSH (follicle-stimulating hormone):

- In the male, LH controls the amount of the hormone testosterone produced by the testes, and FSH controls sperm production.

- In the female, FSH and LH control the levels of the hormones estrogen and progesterone produced by the ovaries; FSH also causes maturation of ova, or eggs, and LH stimulates ovulation—the release of a mature ovum.

During puberty, teens experience growth spurts and other physical changes at different ages and at different rates. **What triggers these changes during adolescence?**

12 Sexuality and You

Secondary Sex Characteristics

During puberty the reproductive organs mature and begin to release the hormones that cause the development of secondary sex characteristics. Secondary sex characteristics are traits that distinguish genders, but are not directly part of the reproductive system. In males, testosterone causes the shoulders to broaden and facial, underarm, and pubic hair to grow. The voice deepens and muscles develop. The bones become longer and larger. In females, estrogen and progesterone cause breast development, growth of underarm and pubic hair, and widened hips.

Along with development of the secondary sex characteristics comes increased activity of the oil and sweat glands. Good hygiene is especially important during this time and will help minimize odor problems.

Good hygiene can help to control acne. Medication may be required in severe cases. Why do you need to pay more attention to personal hygiene during puberty?

Concerns Over Changes During Puberty

Remember that all adolescents experience puberty according to a unique timeline. Growth spurts during puberty depend largely on each person's genetic inheritance and are set in motion by hormones. These hormonal changes cause feelings and sensations never experienced before. It is important to know that everyone grows at a rate that is just right for each individual.

Lesson 3 Review

Facts and Vocabulary

1. What is the endocrine system?

2. What role do hormones play during puberty?

3. Which organs release hormones that cause the development of secondary sex characteristics?

Thinking Critically

4. **Synthesize.** Appraise the significance of physical changes that occur during adolescence. How might the development of secondary sex characteristics affect an adolescent's social and emotional development?

5. **Analyze.** Compare the secondary sex characteristics that develop during puberty for females with those that develop for males.

Applying Health Skills

6. **Stress Management.** A common stressor for teens is to worry over height, weight, or appearance. Make a poster that focuses on how each individual is unique. On the poster, provide a positive tip for handling this stressor, such as thinking positively or being physically active.

Adolescence—A Time of Change **13**

Lesson 3 Review Answers

1. It is a body system made up of ductless glands that secrete chemicals called hormones into the blood.

2. Hormones released by the pituitary gland cause the changes that occur in the body during puberty. These hormones include growth hormones and hormones that affect the brain, glands, skin, bones, muscles, and reproductive organs.

3. The reproductive organs, which are the testes in males and the ovaries in females.

4. Answers will vary but should reflect the student's understanding that developing secondary sex characteristics could affect a teen's self-image and prompt changes in relationships with peers and others.

5. Answers will vary but should include the widening physical differences between males and females. Students may focus on thinking differently about childhood friends of the opposite gender or may emphasize the need for more mature relationship skills.

6. Posters will vary but should indicate an appreciation for the wide variations among adolescents in height, weight, and other developing physical characteristics. The tip for handling the stress of worrying about one's appearance should be practical.

Adolescence—A Time of Change

Active Learning

Class Activity Have students create a chart with the following headings: Male, Female, and Both Genders. Then ask the students to complete the chart by filling in the secondary sex characteristics for each category. Lead a discussion about the similarities and differences between the genders. OL

Critical Thinking

Growth Sequence Growth in puberty proceeds in a specific order: feet, then hands, then arms and legs. Have students explain how this growth sequence contributes to possible awkwardness and/or clumsiness during adolescence. OL

Writing Support

Research Have students find current articles on hormonal research related to growth or the reproductive system. Ask them to write a brief summary of the article. AL

Caption Answer: *Your body increases oil and sweat production, which can cause odor problems.*

ASSESS

Reteaching Have students write a short paragraph describing how the pituitary gland and hormones cause the changes that occur during puberty.

Enrichment Have students do further research on one gland or organ that is part of the endocrine system. Have them make a poster that includes a diagram of the gland or organ and lists its functions. Sum up the lesson by asking volunteers to describe two changes teens experience during puberty.

Assessment Answers

1. The facts will help you understand your growth and development and make decisions that protect your health and prevent some diseases.

2. Examples will vary, but students might suggest deciding not to participate in risky behavior that harms health.

3. Decision-making steps are: 1) State the situation. 2) List the options. 3) Weigh the possible outcomes. 4) Consider values. 5) Make a decision and act on it. 6) Evaluate the decision.

4. Goal-setting steps are: 1) Select a goal and write it down. 2) List the steps you will take to reach your goal. 3) Identify sources of help and support. 4) Set a reasonable time frame for reaching your goal. 5) Evaluate your progress by establishing checkpoints. 6) Reward yourself after achieving your goal.

5. Empathy is the ability to feel what others feel, to put yourself in someone else's place.

6. The pituitary gland does; it is located at the base of the brain.

7. The male organs are the testes; they release testosterone. The female organs are the ovaries; they release estrogen and progesterone.

8. Answers will vary but might include the following: males—shoulders broaden; voice deepens; muscles develop; females— breasts develop; underarm and pubic hair grows; hips widen.

9. Answers will vary, but students could suggest decisions about behaviors such as using tobacco, drinking alcohol, taking illegal drugs, or becoming sexually active. Students should discuss how these decisions could affect all parts of their health.

10. Answers will vary.

11. Answers will vary.

12. Answers will vary but should focus on one of the higher-level thinking skills.

13. Answers will vary, but students should discuss that changes during adolescence occur at different rates.

14. The facial hair signals that this friend has begun to experience the changes of puberty. Answers should include informing the friend that hormones released during puberty cause the sweat glands in the body to become more active. As the sweat glands become more active, body odor can become a problem. The student may suggest to his friend that regular bathing is more necessary now than when they were younger.

15. Pamphlets will vary.

16. Stories will vary.

Reviewing Facts and Vocabulary

1. Why is it important to have factual information about sexuality?

2. Give one example of a decision that could affect your total health in a positive way.

3. Identify the six steps in the decision-making process.

4. List the goal-setting steps.

5. Define *empathy*.

6. What gland controls much of the endocrine system? Where is it located?

7. Identify the male and female reproductive organs that produce sex cells. Which hormones does each organ release?

8. Name three secondary sex characteristics that occur in males and three that occur in females.

Writing Critically

9. Synthesize. Write a specific example of a decision that could affect your physical, mental/emotional, and social well-being.

10. Apply. Select a goal that you worked toward achieving. Write a one-page analysis comparing and contrasting the steps you took in the goal-setting process. Are there any steps in the process that might have helped you attain your goal?

11. Analyze. Choose three of the developmental tasks based on the work of Robert Havighurst. Write an example of an action you can take to succeed at each of them.

12. Analyze. Write a summary identifying a task that you could not perform when you were a child that, because of cognitive development, you can perform now.

13. Evaluate. Write a letter to help a friend who is depressed because he is shorter than all of his peers.

14. Synthesize. You've noticed that your friend has facial hair that he did not have last year. You've also noticed that he develops body odor by the end of the school day. Create a pamphlet showing teens how to recognize the changes that occur during puberty.

Applying Health Skills

15. Advocacy. Create a pamphlet about the importance of making decisions promoting individual, family, and community health. Include examples of appropriate and effective decision-making skills.

16. Practicing Healthful Behaviors. Write a short story that teaches teens the importance of showing responsibility in caring for their physical, mental/emotional, and social health during adolescence.

BEYOND THE CLASSROOM ACTIVITIES

PARENT INVOLVEMENT
Community Programs. With the help of your parent or guardian, contact local programs that provide opportunities for teens to volunteer in the community. Create a reference file listing ways that teens can reach out to others while developing their own emotional and social maturity.

SCHOOL AND COMMUNITY
Endocrine System. Using the Internet or library resources, find out more about the endocrine system. Choose two endocrine glands not discussed in this module. Write a paragraph about each gland, describing the hormone each gland produces and the effect of the hormone on the body.

BEYOND THE CLASSROOM

Parent Involvement: Community Programs. With the help of a parent or guardian, have students contact local programs that provide opportunities for teens to volunteer in the community. Have them create a reference file listing ways that teens can reach out to others while developing their own emotional and social maturity.

School and Community: Endocrine System. Direct students to use the Internet or library resources to find out more about the endocrine system. Have students choose two endocrine glands not discussed in this module and write a paragraph about each gland, describing the hormone each gland produces and the effect of the hormone on the body.

MODULE 2	STANDARDS / NOTES	LESSON ASSESSMENT
	Use this space for standards and notes.	Module 2 Assessment Online assessment
30 MIN. **LESSON 1** **Relationships and Communication** **BIG IDEA.** Establishing values and practicing good communication skills can help you maintain healthy relationships.		Lesson 1 Review Online assessment
30 MIN. **LESSON 2** **Decisions About Sexual Relationships** **BIG IDEA.** Practicing abstinence and using refusal skills can help you avoid potentially risky situations.		Lesson 2 Review Online assessment

Key to Abilities   Teaching Strategies and Activities have been coded for ability level and appropriateness.

AL Activities for students working above grade level

BL Activities for students working below grade level

 OL Activities for students working on grade level

 EL Activities for English Learners

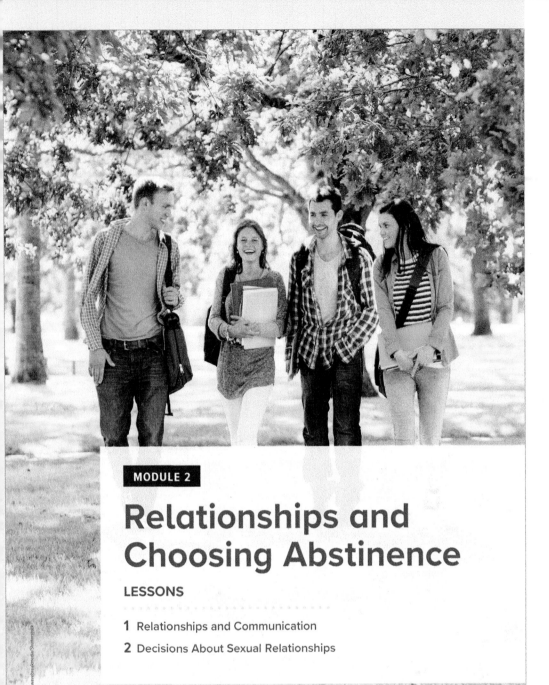

Relationships and Choosing Abstinence

LESSONS

1 Relationships and Communication
2 Decisions About Sexual Relationships

Relationships and Choosing Abstinence

Module Overview Module 1 focuses on building family and peer relationships and developing the communication and refusal skills necessary to practice abstinence in a dating relationship.

LESSON 1
Evaluate the effects of family relationships and peer relationships on physical, mental/emotional, and social health.

LESSON 2
Analyze the benefits of abstinence from sexual activity and evaluate ways to practice abstinence in a dating relationship.

Activating Prior Knowledge

Using Visuals Have students look at the picture on this page. Group dating can help teens feel more relaxed and comfortable in dating situations.
Ask Students: *What are some additional benefits of group dating?*

Relationships and Communication

FOCUS

BIG IDEA Establishing values and practicing good communication skills can help you maintain healthy relationships.

Tell students they will learn more about relationships and communication.

Reading Strategy

Organize Information Students' graphic organizers should include enough details to show that they understand the elements of good communication skill and good listening skills.

QUICKWRITE

Before students answer, write the following on the board for students to answer: *Why do you think communication is important in any relationship?*

Student Objectives

- Evaluate the effects of family relationships on physical, mental/emotional, and social health.
- Evaluate the positive and negative effects of peer relationships.
- Demonstrate communication skills that build and maintain healthy relationships.

TEACH

Health Skills Practice

Decision Making Have students use the decision-making process to evaluate the physical, emotional, and social benefits of abstinence, monogamy, and the avoidance of multiple sexual partners. Have students record their answers in their health journal.

Caption Answer: *Friends who share your interests and respect your personal values play a positive role in your life.*

Active Learning

Class Discussion Ask students to think about their relationships with immediate and extended family members. Point out that people are bonded to family members in many different ways—love, friendship, shared experiences, and values. Ask students how the ways they develop friendships outside their families differ from ways they develop relationships within their families. How are they the same? OL

Relationships and Communication

BEFORE YOU READ

Organize. Create a graphic organizer showing the elements of good communication and good listening skills.

Vocabulary
values
peer pressure
communication
conflict

BIG IDEA Establishing values and practicing good communication skills can help you maintain healthy relationships.

QUICK WRITE

Think about some of healthy relationships you have seen in your life and list three qualities of these relationships. *Write one paragraph explaining why those qualities are important and how having healthy relationships can contribute to a fulfilling life.*

Family and Friends

Humans are social beings. We need other people in our lives. In order to fulfill our basic emotional need to belong, we need to feel that we are valued members of a group. Throughout our lives, we will belong to many different groups.

The first group that most people belong to is their family. The family is the basic unit of society. Besides ensuring that its members' needs for food, clothing, and shelter are met, the family provides guidance and helps children learn to function in society. It is within the family that we first learn to get along with others. Families also teach us our **values**. Values are the beliefs and standards of conduct that are important to a person. Values are also instilled through cultural heritage, religious beliefs, and family traditions. You apply your values to the decisions that you make every day.

As we mature, our experience with society increases. We meet people outside of our family, and we begin to make friends and become a part of other groups. These relationships help us learn about ourselves and others. As we get older, our friendships may change. Some friendships may become deeper, while others may change only slightly. Sometimes we may outgrow relationships.

Friends who share your interests and values can be a source of positive peer pressure. Describe two ways in which a friend might be a positive influence.

Relationships in Adolescence

One of the developmental tasks of adolescence is forming more mature relationships with your peers. This is important for your social health. Many activities during the teen years can broaden and deepen your experience with individuals and groups, helping you to complete this developmental task. Being involved in a variety of school, religious, and community activities can promote your mental/emotional and social growth.

Peer Pressure

As you develop relationships with individuals and groups, you probably will experience **peer pressure**. Peer pressure is the influence that people your own age may have on you. Peer pressure can be positive or negative. For example, members of a school club may encourage each other to develop a special talent. However, a person who takes risks may try to persuade a friend to participate in high-risk behaviors such as using drugs or engaging in sexual activity.

Adolescents with low self-esteem can be particularly influenced by peer pressure. In order to feel a sense of belonging, they may engage in high-risk behaviors or other activities that go against their values.

Dating

During the teen years, dating is often considered an important social activity. Group dates offer teens opportunities to interact with a variety of people while getting to know someone better in an informal setting. Teens may feel less nervous about a first date when they are in a group.

Dating may lead to steady dating, a situation in which two people date each other exclusively. Steady dating may give a person a sense of security, but it may also interfere with developing other healthy relationships. If a relationship doesn't work out, you may think something is wrong with you. This simply is not true. It actually means that the other person has preferences or interests that are different from yours. Although rejection is difficult and breaking up can be painful, it is important not to lose your feelings of self-worth because of another person.

Making Healthy Dating Decisions. An important part of making dating decisions is choosing people with good character. It is difficult to determine the quality of a person's character just by their appearance or popularity. Look for someone who:

- Respects himself or herself.
- Respects others.
- Is unselfish.
- Shares similar values.
- Is kind and caring.

LESSON 1
Relationships and Communication

Critical Thinking

Basic Values Ask students to identify basic values that they consider important. How to these values influence their decisions and their behavior? OL

Reading Strategies

Building Vocabulary Have students write their own definitions of the vocabulary terms and compare them with those in the Glossary/Glosario. OL BL EL

Active Learning

Role Play Let students work in small groups to role-play situations in which teens exert peer pressure. OL

Reading Strategies

Emphasize Point out that group dating is a good way to get to know someone. OL

Active Learning

Class Discussion Discuss with students the advantages of group dating. Brainstorm places in and around your town where people might go on a group date. OL

Critical Thinking

Discuss Review with students the developmental tasks adolescents go through during the teen years. Ask students to discuss the importance of empathy and respect in forming mature peer relationships. OL

LESSON 1
Relationships and Communication

Critical Thinking

Communication Skills Ask students to explain how good communication is essential in mature relationships. Have students think of ways that good communication skills can help them avoid behaviors in which they do not want to participate. OL

Health Skills Practice

Communication Skills After reading the section *Communication,* have two student volunteers role-play the following activity: One person is A, the other is B. Explain that A promises to take B to a concert that starts at 7:30. A says he or she will pick up B at 6:45 but doesn't show up until 8:30. It's too late to go to the concert. B is furious. B is to confront A using "you" statements. After two or three minutes, stop the activity. Have two other student volunteers repeat the scene with B using only "I" messages. Remind the Bs to state how they feel and what they see as the problem. Allow two to three minutes. In a discussion, have students compare how B felt each time and how A felt each time. **Usually there is less finger pointing and less defensiveness the second time.** OL

Cooperative Learning

Nonverbal Communication Have each student bring in a picture from a magazine that is an example of nonverbal communication. Each student should write on the back of the picture what he or she thinks is being communicated. Tell students that there are no wrong answers for this activity. Allow each student to hold up his or her picture for the rest of the class to see. Call on two or three volunteers to say what they think is being communicated in the picture. Then, let the student read his or her remarks from the back of the photograph. Point out that different people can get different messages from nonverbal communication. The same is true for verbal, or spoken communication. That is why it is important to practice the rules of good communication. AL

Caption Answer: *Sample answer: Effective communicators use "I" messages and their body language matches their words.*

Communication

Communication is the process through which you send messages to and receive messages from others. It is essential to any relationship. Good communication skills will help you keep relationships healthy and form more mature relationships with your peers. Good communication means clearly expressing your feelings, thoughts, ideas, and expectations. Here are some suggestions for improving your communication skills. Practice these skills when there is no problem in the relationship, and you will be more likely to use them when a problem does arise.

1. Use "I" messages to avoid placing blame.
2. Maintain a polite tone in your voice.
3. Speak directly to the person.
4. Provide a clear, organized message that states the situation.
5. Body language should match your words.

By using "I" messages, you are taking responsibility for how you feel. "You" statements, such as "You are rude when you keep me waiting," send the message that you are blaming someone else. When people are blamed or accused of something, they usually become defensive. This causes conflict. When you use an "I" message, such as "I understood we were meeting at four o'clock, and I am unhappy that I had to wait two hours," others have no need to be defensive and are more likely to discuss the issue.

Declining a Date

As you begin to date, you will be asked on a date by someone you are not interested in dating. You should not feel that you must say yes. However, if you decide to say no, try to do so in a way that won't hurt the person's feelings. Remember that it took courage for the person to approach you. Think about the times that you asked someone out on a date. Asking another person out on a date takes courage. The person who asks is expressing feelings of affection and a desire to learn more about another person. It's okay that those feelings aren't shared, however that's not a reason to hurt someone else's feelings.

Keep in mind that some teens may feel ready to date while others do not. No one should feel pressured to go on a date before he or she feels ready. It is also a good idea to wait until you feel comfortable dating. One option is to go on group dates when you first begin dating. Group dates can help a shy teen ease into dating slowly. In a group, one person may not feel awkward because he or she can't keep the conversation going.

Effective communicators are able to state the situation clearly. **What are other skills effective communicators use?**

18 Relationships and Choosing Abstinence

Good Listening Skills

Good communication also means listening to what other people say. Everyone wants to feel that he or she is being heard and is not going to be judged, interrupted, or ignored. Follow these guidelines for being a good listener:

- Give your full attention to the speaker. Eliminate distractions such as texting or television.

- Focus on the speaker's message. Look for the central concept that the speaker is trying to convey.

- Indicate your interest. Lean toward the speaker; nod at or encourage the other person. Maintain eye contact.

- Remember what the speaker has said. When it's your turn to speak, summarize your understanding of what the other person has said. If you have misunderstood, the speaker can correct you.

- Use positive body language. A smile and a nod indicate that you are interested and open to communication.

Conflict

Whether relationships are close or merely casual, **conflicts** are always going to occur. A conflict is a disagreement, struggle, or fight. Some of the most common reasons for conflict include a lack of communication between two people and their attempts to meet different needs. When conflicts or disagreements occur, relying on the T.A.L.K. strategy will help both parties reach a peaceful resolution.

1. T—Take time out.
2. A—Allow each person to express his or her opinion uninterrupted.
3. L—Let each person take turns asking questions and clarifying any statements.
4. K—Keep brainstorming to find a good solution.

Compromise, or give-and-take, is essential to every healthy relationship. When both people or both sides feel like winners in a conflict, everyone benefits. For example, friends might agree to alternate activities when spending time together so that each person has a chance to choose an activity.

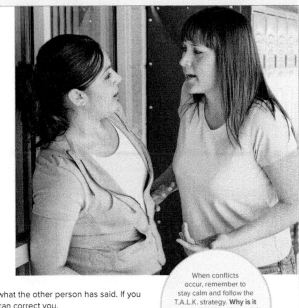

When conflicts occur, remember to stay calm and follow the T.A.L.K. strategy. **Why is it important to take time out if the individuals involved in a conflict are feeling emotional or upset?**

Did You Know

Communication in a relationship can be improved if both people understand their rights. In any relationship, you have a right to do the following:

- Make your own decisions.
- Ask for what you want.
- Be treated with respect.
- Say no without feeling guilty.
- Express your thoughts and feelings.
- Protect your health and safety.

LESSON 1
Relationships and Communication

Reading Strategy

Analyzing After students read the section Good Listening Skills, have each pick one skill he or she needs to work on. Ask each to make a plan describing what he or she will do to improve this skill. OL

Emphasize Stress that conflicts are normal in any kind of relationship. It is important to have a strategy to deal with conflicts before they occur. OL

Active Learning

Compromising Have students describe examples of times that they worked out a compromise with someone. Ask them to explain how the compromise was to their advantage, and how they think it affected their relationship with the other person. OL

Caption Answer: *Sample answer: Take time out so both people can calm down and reach a peaceful resolution.*

Relationships and Communication

Critical Thinking

Self-Concept Discuss how self-concept affects one's ability to have healthy relationships. OL

Analyzing Ask students to think about why a couple might want to see each other exclusively. Ask students to list these reasons on a piece of paper and identify them as healthy or unhealthy reasons. Look at students' responses and share appropriate ones with the class for discussion. OL

Active Learning

Group Dating Have students write a story that describes a successful group date. The story should tell what the group does, where it goes, and so on. Collect the papers, choose some that are suitable, and read them to the class. OL

Cultural Awareness

Healthy Relationships Have students find current articles or examples from others that describe healthy relationships. Encourage them to include family relationships, as well as friendships and dating relationships. AL

Caption Answer: *Sample answer: Good communication is important so you can resolve conflicts without compromising values.*

ASSESS

Progress Monitoring

Reteaching Have students reread the five suggestions for good communication. Have them explain in their own words how they would approach a particular conflict with a friend. Explain that good communication skills can be used to resolve conflicts with people they are close to and others whom they don't know as well.

Enrichment Divide the class into males and females. Have each group make a list of the five qualities they look for in a friend. Have the class compare lists. Then have them discuss the following question: *How do the qualities change when considering someone to date?*

Summarize this lesson by telling students that the material in this lesson presented skills to help them communicate well and build healthy relationships. In the next lesson, they will learn about making decisions about sexual relationships.

Conflict and Dating

Becoming skilled at "choosing your battles," or deciding when it is worthwhile to take a stand, can help you avoid unnecessary conflict. Determine if the issue is really important and if it will matter tomorrow, next week, or next month. Thoughtful evaluation of the situation will help you decide if there truly is a conflict. Then you can use the T.A.L.K. strategy to resolve a conflict without compromising your values.

In any relationship, people must communicate in order to have their feelings known and understood. Good communication is especially important in a dating relationship. Both people on a date must be willing to express themselves honestly and listen to what the other person is saying.

Suppose you are on a date with someone you really like. You've spent time getting to know each other, and you have fun together. What are some expectations you might have of the person you are dating? How would your date know what your expectations are? Conflict can occur when two people's expectations are different and are not clearly communicated. Effective communication will help you maintain healthy, mature relationships.

Teens in a dating relationship should identify a variety of activities both can enjoy. What are other strategies for maintaining a healthy dating relationship?

Lesson 1 Review

Facts and Vocabulary

1. Evaluate ways your parents, guardians, and other family members contribute to physical and mental/emotional health and help you establish healthy relationships.

2. Define the term peer pressure and evaluate the positive and negative effects of relationships with peers.

3. List three benefits of group dating.

Thinking Critically

4. **Analyze.** Explain and demonstrate the importance of using good communication skills in building and maintaining healthy relationships. Give two examples.

5. **Synthesize.** Make a list of positive ways you can develop healthy relationships with your peers. Describe specific actions you can take to become a good friend.

Applying Health Skills

6. **Analyzing Influences.** Create a pair of lists. Label the first list "Family" and the second one "Peers." In each section, list the ways in which that group of people has influenced you in your relationships. Provide at least two specific examples for each list. Evaluate whether the influence on your behavior was positive or negative.

20 Relationships and Choosing Abstinence

Lesson 1 Review Answers

1. Parents, guardians, and other family members help you learn to get along with other people. Your family teaches you your basic values and helps you learn to function in society.

2. Peer pressure is the influence that people your own age may have on you. A teen with low self-esteem is more likely to conform to peer pressure even if it means engaging in high-risk behaviors or other activities that go against his or her values.

3. Benefits include: You have opportunities to interact with a variety of people; you can get to know individuals better at the same time; and you may feel less nervous on a first date.

4. If you use good communication skills, you will find it easier to talk calmly about a problem. For example, if you use "I" messages, you are less likely to provoke a conflict by making the other person feel blamed.

5. Answers will vary but might include examples of a variety of social activities. Becoming a good friend might involve helping your friend with a task or a project and using good communication and listening skills.

6. Answers will vary.

Decisions About Sexual Relationships

BIG IDEA Practicing abstinence and using refusal skills can help you avoid potentially risky situations.

QUICK WRITE

Describe a decision that a teen in a dating relationship may have to make. Apply the steps of the decision-making process to help the teen make a healthful choice.

Decisions About Sexual Behavior

Good communication between people who are dating is critical for setting limits about sexual activity. Each person must decide what he or she wants from the relationship and communicate those decisions. New and sometimes confusing feelings, especially physical attraction to another person, may complicate these decisions. It is important to recognize that being physically attracted to someone and being in love are not the same thing. Infatuation, or exaggerated feelings of passion for another person, can sometimes be mistaken for love.

It is perfectly normal for young people to decide that they are not ready for a sexual relationship. As a matter of fact, many teens are making the choice to practice **abstinence**. Abstinence is a deliberate decision to avoid harmful behaviors, including sexual activity and the use of alcohol, tobacco, and other drugs.

Your family may already have set limits regarding romantic relationships. Remember that seeking advice and feedback from parents or guardians is an important part of the decision-making process as you mature. They can help you determine how to set your own limits.

Abstinence from sexual activity is the safe, healthy choice for teens. It is the only method that is 100 percent effective in preventing unplanned pregnancy, sexually transmitted diseases (STDs), and the sexual transmission of HIV/AIDS. However, some abstinent teens may feel pressured by their peers to become sexually involved. Sometimes peer pressure may lead teens to boast about imaginary sexual experiences in an attempt to impress others.

BEFORE YOU READ

Explain. Write a summary describing the types of decisions you think teens must make about sexual relationships.

Vocabulary

abstinence
consent
affirmative consent
intimacy
refusal skills

Mature teens effectively communicate their decisions about sexual limits. **What are some healthful ways for dating teens to demonstrate respect for each other's decisions?**

Decisions About Sexual Relationships 21

LESSON 2
Decisions About Sexual Relationships

FOCUS

BIG IDEA Practicing abstinence and using refusal skills can help you avoid potentially risky situations.

Have students share their reasons for practicing abstinence. Explain that in this lesson students will study reasons to wait until marriage to engage in sexual activity.

Reading Strategy

Explain Student's answers will vary.

QUICKWRITE

Before students answer, write the following on the board for students to answer: *List three reasons for teens to practice abstinence from sexual activity.* **Accept reasonable responses.**

Student Objectives

- Analyze the benefits of abstinence from sexual activity.
- Evaluate ways to practice abstinence in a dating relationship.
- Demonstrate refusal skills to reinforce the decision to remain abstinent.

TEACH

Active Learning

Research Have students conduct research to find out if there are local or national organizations formed to encourage abstinence. Ask students to design their own organization and describe ways it would help members in their commitment to remain abstinent. OL

Caption Answer: *Sample answer: Choose activities both people can enjoy that do not compromise the person's values.*

Decisions About Sexual Relationships

Reading Strategy

Building Vocabulary Have students write their own definitions of what they believe intimacy and refusal skills might be. Have them look up the words in the Glossary/Glosario and compare the actual definition to their own. Emphasize that intimacy involves physical and emotional closeness. Tell students they will learn more about intimacy and its relationship to abstinence. OL **EL**

Critical Thinking

Affirmative Consent Lead a class discussion regarding the topic of Affirmative Consent to make sure students know what the concept means. Questions might include: 1. What does the term "Affirmative Consent" mean? **A person says yes without being forced or threatened.** 2. Explain why a person cannot give affirmative consent if he or she is threatened. **The person is only agreeing to the activity because of the threat.** 3. How is the statement "If you won't have sex with me, I'll break up with you" a threat? Can a person still give affirmative consent if this statement is made? **One person is forcing the other person to say yes, so the consent is not given freely.** OL

Messages about sexual behavior come from many different sources— peers, magazines, books, music, television, and movies—and are often confusing and contradictory. How can you decide for yourself about remaining abstinent? Ask yourself the following questions:

- Have I communicated with my boyfriend/girlfriend about my expectations in this relationship?
- Do my boyfriend's/girlfriend's beliefs about sexual activity differ from my own?
- Does my boyfriend/girlfriend pressure me to engage in behaviors that I'm uncomfortable with?
- How would I feel about myself if I engaged in sexual activity?
- Am I prepared to deal with an unplanned pregnancy?
- What would I do if I found out I had an STD?
- How would I handle being infected with HIV, the virus that causes AIDS?

Sexual Activity and Consent

Sexual activity includes two layers of **consent**. Consent is permission or agreement for something to happen. Each state has a law that defines the age of consent in that state. A teen who is under the age of consent cannot legally agree to become sexually active. If one person is under the age of consent, the other person can be charged with a crime. To find the age of consent for your state, go online to your state's legislature.

Getting consent means that a couple must stop while they are sexually aroused, and determine whether both of them give consent for sexual activity to begin. Both people must agree to give consent. If not, sexual activity should not take place. In some states, partners are required to obtain **affirmative consent**, or "yes means yes" consent. Affirmative consent is the clear and voluntary agreement to engage in sexual activity. Giving or refusing consent requires the use of communications skills. Each person should communicate their feelings assertively. They should also listen to each other. If one person says no, the other person must stop.

Consent should be freely given. This means that both parties agree to engage in sexual activity. One person should not intimidate or threaten the other person to become sexually active. If threats or intimidation are used the request for sexual activity becomes coercion. If this occurs, affirmative consent is not granted. Consent cannot be freely given if a person is coerced.

Affirmative consent cannot be given if a person who is under the influence of drugs or alcohol. When a person is under the influence of a substance, he or she cannot give consent freely. If sexual activity occurs, it is rape and is considered a crime. The person who did not give consent may suffer from physical injury. That person will also face mental/emotional consequences when dealing with the effects of the crime. The person who initiated sexual activity can face legal consequences. That person could be charged with sexual assault or rape, and may spend time in jail.

Practicing Abstinence

By carefully considering and honestly answering the questions on the previous screen, many teens make the healthful decision to practice abstinence until marriage. Abstinence does not mean there will be no **intimacy**, or physical contact or closeness, in a relationship. For example, a couple can hold hands, hug, kiss, and grow to know and understand each other while practicing abstinence. When teens choose abstinence, they are demonstrating the ability to take responsibility for their health and well-being.

Benefits of Abstinence

Young people have identified a variety of reasons to remain abstinent until marriage, including the following benefits to their physical, mental/emotional, and social health:

- Abstinence eliminates both persons' risk of contracting an STD, including HIV/AIDS.

Practicing abstinence requires genuine commitment. **How can dating in groups help teens keep a commitment to be abstinent?**

Fancy Collection/SuperStock

Decisions About Sexual Relationships **23**

Reading Strategy

Emphasize It is very important for a person practicing abstinence to communicate honestly and clearly with his or her date or girlfriend/boyfriend. To do this, an individual must be clear as to why he or she is choosing abstinence. OL

Critical Thinking

Discuss How can being sexually active interfere with a teen's plans for the future? Remind students of the risks of pregnancy and sexually transmitted diseases. OL

Caption Answer: *Sample answer: Group dating encourages conversation and puts less pressure on teens to engage in sexual activity.*

LESSON 2
Decisions About Sexual Relationships

Critical Thinking

Age of Consent In this section, the text describes the age of consent and sexual conduct by minors. In many states, the law sets the age of consent at 18. Any person under the age of 18 cannot legally agree to become sexually active. If a person over the age of 18 becomes sexually active with a person under the age of 18, the older person can be charged with a crime. Some states have what is commonly referred to as a *Romeo-Juliet Law*. This law would prohibit two teens who are both under the age of 18 from being charged with a crime. In states without these exceptions, if two teens who are both under the age of 18 become sexually active together, both can be charged with breaching the age of consent.

Class Discussion Ask students why states might set an age of consent law? Who does the law protect? **Explain to students that age of consent laws protect young teens who may be susceptible to the influence of people older than they are. Older teens and adults who have influence over younger teens might convince them to become sexually active before they feel ready. The law also protects teens from predators, who might target young teens.** OL

- Abstinence is the only 100 percent effective method to avoid unplanned pregnancy.
- Becoming sexually active goes against their personal values.
- Abstinence can allow a couple to build a deeper friendship.

Most teens are not physically, mentally, emotionally, or financially ready for the short-term and long-term consequences of engaging in sexual activity. In addition to the effects on physical and mental/emotional health, there can be legal consequences. It is illegal for an adult to have sexual contact with anyone under the age of consent, which varies from state to state. In many states, it is illegal for unmarried minors to engage in sexual activity. These negative effects can disrupt a teen's life and interfere with any plans for the future.

Practicing Your Decision to Be Abstinent

If you have made the decision to abstain from sexual activity, a well-thought-out plan of action will help you uphold that choice. The following steps can help you.

- Make a detailed list of your reasons for choosing abstinence.
- Discuss your feelings, your decision, and your expectations of the relationship with your boyfriend or girlfriend.
- Place yourself in situations that reinforce your decision to be abstinent. When dating, choose places to go that encourage conversation, or date in groups.
- Plan your time together—where you will go, how long you will stay, and what time you will go home.

Using Refusal Skills

As you mature, you will assume more and more responsibility for your actions. This means that you always try to make the best possible decisions for your health, safety, and well-being. Sometimes, however, you may feel pressured to make risky decisions that go against your values. In these situations, you will need to stand up for yourself and firmly say no. **Refusal skills** are communication strategies that help you say no effectively when you are urged to take part in behaviors that are unsafe or unhealthful, or go against your values. Practicing refusal skills will help you uphold your intentions and values. Follow these tips to strengthen your refusal skills.

- Use decision-making skills.
- When resisting pressure, simply say no without feeling that you need to justify yourself. Repeat yourself if necessary.
- Do not insult or yell at the other person, but do use a firm tone of voice and direct eye contact. To help show that you mean what you say, avoid body language that implies you are nervous or unsure.

- Do not compromise when you feel strongly about something. Compromise may lead someone to think you will change your mind under increased pressure.

- Avoid the use of alcohol and other drugs. The use of these substances impairs your judgment and your ability to make healthy decisions.

- If the other person persists and continues to pressure you, *leave*. Go someplace where you feel safe and comfortable.

Whenever you use refusal skills, congratulate yourself for standing up for what you believe in. You will feel stronger for not compromising your values. Remember, true friends will not challenge you to do something that goes against your values. Develop friendships with people who share your values and interests. They will not push you to do something you don't want to do. They will respect your ability to make the right decision for yourself. You will find it's much easier to resist negative peer pressure from someone else when you have friends who stand by you and support your decision.

Character Check

When you make the decision to practice abstinence, you are demonstrating respect for your body. In what other ways does practicing abstinence demonstrate respect for self and others? Summarize your thoughts in your notebook.

Developing strong friendships with people who share and respect your values will help strengthen your decision to practice abstinence.

Lesson 2 Review

Facts and Vocabulary

1. Define *abstinence*.

2. Analyze the importance and benefits of abstinence. Discuss how it can promote emotional health and prevent unplanned pregnancy, STDs, and HIV/AIDS.

3. Describe three refusal skills you can use to reinforce a decision to remain abstinent. Give an example of each skill.

Thinking Critically

4. **Evaluate.** What would you say to a friend who says that he will make a decision about sexual activity when faced with the problem, not before it comes up? Explain your reasoning.

5. **Apply.** Engaging in sexual activity before marriage can have physical, mental/emotional, and legal consequences. Provide two examples of each of these types of consequences.

Applying Health Skills

6. **Practicing Healthful Behaviors.** Write a script for a scenario involving someone who is using the refusal skills covered in this lesson to maintain her choice to be abstinent in a dating relationship.

Decisions About Sexual Relationships **25**

Health Skills Practice

Refusal Skills Ask students why it might be more difficult to say "no" to someone you care about than to a casual acquaintance. Have them think of ways they can refuse a friend while still showing that they care about that person. OL

Active Learning

Demonstrating After reading the section on refusal skills, allow students to meet in groups to role-play teens using refusal skills to say "no" to high risk behaviors, such as drinking alcohol. OL

ASSESS

Reteaching Have students use their own words to describe refusal skills.

Enrichment Have students write a letter to a younger family member or neighbor in which they coach the younger person on a specific situation requiring the use of refusal skills. Students should also remind the younger person of their rights in a relationship.

Sum up the lesson by asking students to list the three most important things they learned in this lesson.

Lesson 2 Review Answers

1. Abstinence is a deliberate decision to avoid harmful behaviors.

2. Sample Answer: Abstinence can allow a couple to build a deeper friendship; abstinence eliminates both persons' risks of contracting a sexually transmitted disease; abstinence is the only 100 percent effective method to avoid unplanned pregnancy.

3. Any three of the following: Say no, repeat yourself if necessary; be polite but firm; suggest alternative activities; do not compromise.

4. Answers will vary. Students may suggest to their friend that it is easier to decide about limits on sexual behavior before he or she is in a situation where sexual feelings build up.

5. Answers will vary. Possible physical consequences include STDs and unplanned pregnancy. Possible emotional consequences include feelings of guilt and anxiety. Legal consequences exist for any adult who has sexual contact with anyone under the age of consent.

6. Answers will vary. Plays should feature appropriate dating situations.

MODULE 2
Assessment Answers

1. Family

2. Communication is the process through which you send messages to and receive messages from others.

3. By using an "I" message, you are taking responsibility for your feelings. A "you" statement seems to blame someone else and can cause the listener to become defensive and unwilling to talk about the problem.

4. Any four of the following: Give your full attention to the person speaking and eliminate distractions; focus on the speaker's message by looking for the central concept; indicate your interest; remember what the speaker has said; use positive body language.

5. Issues to consider include: pressure from a boyfriend or girlfriend to engage in sexual activity; differing from a boyfriend or girlfriend regarding feelings about premarital sexual activity; the benefits of abstinence; communication about expectations of the relationship with a boyfriend or girlfriend; and the effects of engaging in sexual activity on the teen and his or her family.

6. Intimacy is closeness between two people that develops over time. A couple can hold hands, hug, kiss, and grow to know and understand each other to establish intimacy while practicing abstinence.

7. You can plan the location of the date, the amount of time that you will spend on the date, and when you will go home. Answers will vary, but may discuss how planning safe activities can help teens avoid risky situations.

8. Refusal skills are communication strategies that help you say no effectively.

9. Charts will vary. Students may list values such as honesty, trust, and respect.

10. Peer pressure can have a positive effect if friends also practice abstinence themselves. Peer pressure can have a negative effect if sexually active friends make a person feel that he or she needs to change behavior to belong to the group.

11. Answers will vary. Students may suggest that if the dating partner does not respect the person's decision, he or she may not be right for the person.

12. Answers will vary. Student responses should incorporate the following: dating someone who shares interests and values; using good communication skills; learning how to resolve conflict without compromising values; and deciding in advance their personal limits on sexual behavior.

13. Answers will vary. Student responses should incorporate the ideas of setting guidelines in advance, avoiding high-risk situations, and using refusal skills.

14. Skits will vary.

15. Stories will vary.

16. Pamphlets will vary.

Reviewing Facts and Vocabulary

1. What basic social unit serves as the foundation for your values?

2. Define the term *communication*.

3. Why is it important to use "I" messages when discussing an issue or giving an opinion?

4. List four ways that you can practice good listening skills.

5. Describe the issues that a teen might consider when making decisions about remaining abstinent.

6. What is *intimacy*? Explain how a couple can establish intimacy while practicing abstinence.

7. What aspects of a date can you plan in advance, and how might such planning help you avoid high-risk situations?

8. What are *refusal skills*?

Writing Critically

9. Synthesize. Values develop from many different sources, including your family, your religious beliefs, your personal experiences, and your cultural heritage. Make a two-column chart. In the left column, list ten values that are important to you. In the right column, identify the people or experiences that helped you to form these values.

10. Synthesize. Write a one-page summary explaining how peer pressure can have a positive or a negative effect on a person's decision to remain abstinent.

11. Evaluate. What healthful alternatives would you recommend to someone who is considering giving in to sexual pressure from a girlfriend or boyfriend?

12. Analyze. Write a paragraph describing ways that communication skills and refusal skills can help teens maintain healthy dating relationships.

13. Synthesize. Jackie has agreed to go to the prom with Ryan. She wants to remain abstinent, but she is extremely attracted to Ryan. She has a feeling that he will pressure her to engage in sexual activity. What advice might you give her?

Applying Health Skills

14. Communication Skills. Create a skit with dialogue in which two teens reach an agreement on where to go on a date. Act out the skit with a partner, using polite tones and body language to match the words in the skit.

15. Decision Making. Write a short story that teaches teens the importance of making responsible decisions about sexual relationships.

16. Advocacy. Create a pamphlet that encourages teens to practice abstinence. Include examples of appropriate and effective communication skills. Be sure to use catchy headlines, graphics, and other visuals to engage the reader.

BEYOND THE CLASSROOM ACTIVITIES

PARENT INVOLVEMENT
Group Activities. Research where teens in your community can go on group dates that involve safe and healthy activities. Draw a map of your town or city that shows where these places are located.

SCHOOL AND COMMUNITY
Thinking of the Future. Research the difficulties that teens face when they experience an unplanned pregnancy. Find out how having a baby affects a teen's education, finances, and social life.

BEYOND THE CLASSROOM

Parent Involvement: Group Activities. Have students research places that teens in their community can go on group dates that involve safe and healthy activities. Have them create maps of their town or city that shows where these places are located.

School and Community: Thinking of the Future. Have students research the difficulties teens face when they experience an unplanned pregnancy. Students should focus on how having a baby affects a teen's education, finances, and social life.

- Encourage students to participate in activities that involve parents and community resources.
- Answers will vary.

MODULE 3	STANDARDS / NOTES	LESSON ASSESSMENT
	Use this space for standards and notes.	Module 3 Assessment Online assessment
LESSON 1 **The Male Reproductive System** **BIG IDEA.** The purpose of the male reproductive organs is to protect, store, and help move the sperm. *30 MIN.*		Lesson 1 Review Online assessment
LESSON 2 **The Female Reproductive System** **BIG IDEA.** The female reproductive system matures during puberty, and can then create new life. *30 MIN.*		Lesson 2 Review Online assessment
LESSON 3 **Hormones and Sexual Feelings** **BIG IDEA.** Sexual feelings are a result of hormones and are normal and healthy. *30 MIN.*		Lesson 3 Review Online assessment

Key to Abilities   Teaching Strategies and Activities have been coded for ability level and appropriateness.

AL Activities for students working above grade level

BL Activities for students working below grade level

OL Activities for students working on grade level

EL Activities for English Learners

The Reproductive System

MODULE 3

The Reproductive System

LESSONS

1 The Male Reproductive System

2 The Female Reproductive System

3 Hormones and Sexual Feelings

27

Module Overview Module 1 focuses on the importance of good hygiene and disease prevention, as well as the functions of the female and male reproductive system.

LESSON 1
Describe the function of the male reproductive system and recognize the importance of early detection and treatment of health issues.

LESSON 2
Describe the function of the female reproductive system and recognize the importance of early detection and treatment of health issues.

LESSON 3
Examine the effect of hormones on body systems and sexual feelings.

Activating Prior Knowledge

Using Visuals Many changes occur during the teen years. Hormones control these physical and emotional changes.

Ask Students: *How can keeping your health triangle in balance help you through the changes of adolescence?*

The Male Reproductive System

FOCUS

BIG IDEA The purpose of the male reproductive organs is to protect, store, and help move the sperm. Tell students that their reproductive systems are inactive until puberty. Then the reproductive systems of both males and females change and begin to function. This is why it is especially important at this time for adolescents to learn how the reproductive systems work and how to care for them. Students may discuss personal hygiene and monthly self-examinations.

Reading Strategy

Organize Information Students' graphic organizers should include enough details to show that they understand the internal and external structure of the male reproductive system.

QUICKWRITE

Before students answer, write the following on the board for students to answer: *How can you take care of your reproductive system?* **Accept reasonable responses.**

Student Objectives

- Analyze the relationship between good personal hygiene, health promotion, and disease prevention.
- Describe the functioning of the male reproductive system.
- Recognize the importance of early detection in the treatment of conditions of the male reproductive system.

TEACH

Active Learning

Class Activity Review the parts of the male reproductive system. Have students examine the path of the sperm on the illustration of the male reproductive system. Tell them that sperm are produced in the testes and then move to the epididymis at the back of the testes, where they mature. The sperm then travel into the vas deferens, which becomes the ejaculatory duct as it passes through the prostate gland. Secretions from the seminal vesicles empty into the ejaculatory duct and join with the sperm and secretions from the testes. Secretions from the prostate gland and Cowper's glands are the final components that make up semen. The ejaculatory duct opens into the urethra, through which the semen exits the body. OL

The Male Reproductive System

BEFORE YOU READ

Organize Information. Create a graphic organizer listing the external and internal male reproductive organs.

Vocabulary

testosterone
sperm
testes
scrotum
epididymis
penis
erection
semen
ejaculation
vas deferens

BIG IDEA The purpose of the male reproductive organs is to protect, store, and help move the sperm.

QUICK WRITE

Fold a sheet of paper into thirds. List the external male reproductive organs in the first column. List the internal male reproductive organs in the second column. *Write down any questions you have about the structure and function of the male reproductive system in the third column.*

External Male Reproductive Organs

The testes (also called testicles), scrotum, and the penis are the external male reproductive organs. Each has its own role to play in the structure and function of the male reproductive system.

The Scrotum and Testes

Testosterone is the male sex hormone produced by the testes. It controls the production of **sperm,** which are male reproductive cells. A mature male can produce millions of sperm daily. To do this, the temperature of the **testes,** which are the male sex glands, must be a few degrees lower than the normal body temperature of 98.6 degrees F. The **scrotum** keeps the testes at the right temperature by holding them either away from or close to the body as needed. The scrotum is a loose sac of skin that extends outside the body and contains the testes. When body temperature rises, muscles attached to the scrotum relax, lowering the testes away from the body. When body temperature drops, the muscles tighten and the testes move closer to the body for warmth.

Sperm are produced in a section of the testes called the seminiferous tubules. There are about 800 of these threadlike tubes in each testis that produce thousands of sperm every second. Once sperm are produced, they move into the **epididymis,** which is a highly coiled structure located on the back side of each testis. Maturation of the sperm continues in the epididymis and takes about 64 days.

A mature sperm is one of the smallest cells in the body. Each sperm carries 23 chromosomes, half the number present in other body cells. A female egg cell, or ovum, also carries 23 chromosomes. When a sperm unites with a female egg cell, the result is one cell with 46 chromosomes, leading to the production of a human embryo.

The Penis

The **penis** is a tube-like organ that functions in both sexual reproduction and the elimination of urine. When sponge-like tissue in the penis fills with blood, the penis becomes erect, or enlarged and hard. **Erections** are a normal part of being a male. They occur more easily and more often during puberty.

The penis must be erect for **semen** to leave the body. Semen is a mixture of sperm and glandular secretions. The release of semen from the penis is called **ejaculation**. As many as 300 million to 500 million sperm are released in the average ejaculation. Fertilization—the joining of a male sperm cell and a female egg cell—can result if ejaculation occurs during sexual intercourse. Erection, however, does not mean that semen must be released; the penis will return to its un-erect state without ejaculation.

All male babies are born with a fold of skin, known as foreskin, which covers the end of the penis. Surgical removal of the foreskin is called circumcision. Circumcisions are performed for religious and cultural reasons. For many years, they were also performed because they were thought to be necessary to prevent infection. However, circumcision is not medically necessary with good personal hygiene.

Internal Male Reproductive Organs

The internal male reproductive structures play important roles in the male reproductive system. These structures include the vas deferens, the urethra, the seminal vesicles, the prostate gland, and Cowper's glands.

The Vas Deferens and Urethra

After sperm mature in the epididymis of a testis, they travel into the **vas deferens**. This is a long tube that connects each epididymis with the urethra. Lined with smooth muscle that contracts to move sperm through the duct, the vas deferens is the main carrier of sperm. Viable sperm can remain in this duct for several months.

The vas deferens loops over the pubic bone, around the bladder, and through the prostate gland. It is 16 to 18 inches long. As it passes through the prostate gland, it narrows and becomes the ejaculatory duct, which opens into the urethra. As sperm travel through these ducts, they mix with several fluids to form semen.

The urethra is a duct that extends six to eight inches from the urinary bladder, through the prostate, and to the tip of the penis. The urethra carries urine from the bladder out of the body; it also carries semen out of the body. Although the urethra carries both urine and semen, it is physically impossible to carry both at the same time. When the penis becomes erect, a ring of muscular tissue closes off the bladder and keeps urine from entering the urethra.

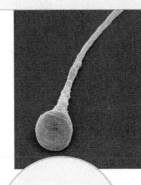

Sperm can be seen only under a microscope. Each sperm consists of a head, a midpiece, and a tail that moves it through the various ducts and out of the body. **Where are sperm produced?**

The Male Reproductive System

Reading Strategy

Building Vocabulary Have students look over the list of vocabulary words and note any similarities between the words they can find. Some of these similarities may be obvious, such as *testes* and *testosterone*. Tell students that the word *epididymis* comes from the Greek word *didymos,* meaning "testis." Have them find other words in the list that relate to one another. OL BL EL

Emphasize Help students understand that keeping the temperature of the testes within a fairly narrow range allows normal sperm formation. The distance between the scrotum and the body changes; the skin of the scrotum tightens up to bring the testes closer to the body to increase heat and loosens to move the testes farther away from the body to reduce heat. OL

Critical Thinking

Discuss The head of a sperm includes enzymes needed to enter the ovum. Have students consider how this process might work and why it is important. OL

Caption Answer: *The seminiferous tubes.*

The Male Reproductive System

Reading Strategy

Emphasize Point out that semen is a complex mixture of sperm and several secretions that keep sperm alive and active as they make their way out of the body. OL

Critical Thinking

Discuss Enlargement of the prostate is a common problem for older males. Have students consider possible effects this might have on the ducts that pass through the prostate. OL

Caption Answer: *These structures include the vas deferens, the urethra, the seminal vesicles, the prostate gland, and Cowper's glands.*

The Male Reproductive System

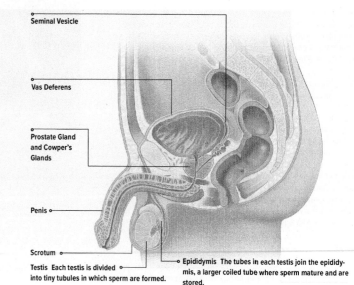

Seminal Vesicle

Vas Deferens

Prostate Gland and Cowper's Glands

Penis

Scrotum

Testis Each testis is divided into tiny tubules in which sperm are formed.

Epididymis The tubes in each testis join the epididymis, a larger coiled tube where sperm mature and are stored.

The internal male reproductive structures play important roles in the male reproductive system. What are the internal structures of the male reproductive system?

The Reproductive Glands

The purpose of the glands in the reproductive system is to add secretions that support the sperm as they move through the system. Semen consists of sperm and secretions from the testes, the seminal vesicles, the prostate gland, and Cowper's glands.

- **Seminal Vesicles.** The seminal vesicles, or sacs, are located on either side of the prostate gland, and each measures about two inches in length. The secretions from the seminal vesicles help make sperm mobile and provide them with nourishment. The secretions from the seminal vesicles empty into the ejaculatory ducts. They then travel into the urethra with the sperm and other testicular secretions.

- **Prostate Gland.** The prostate gland lies just below the bladder and surrounds the urethra. It is about the size of a walnut. This gland secretes a milky, alkaline fluid that mixes with sperm. Acids would destroy the sperm, but the fluid from the prostate gland helps neutralize the acids found in the urethra and also those encountered in the female's vagina during intercourse.

- **Cowper's Glands.** These two pea-sized glands sit just below the prostate gland and open into the urethra. Cowper's glands secrete a clear mucus into the urethra. This secretion, known as pre-ejaculation, is also alkaline and helps carry and protect sperm by lubricating the urethra and neutralizing the acidity of any urine.

The Male Reproductive System

Reading Strategy

Emphasize Males need to wear protective gear during sports to protect the reproductive organs from serious injury. OL

Caption Answer: *This is best done during or after bathing, when the skin of the scrotum is relaxed.*

Concerns About the Male Reproductive Organs

Nocturnal emissions, hernia, sterility, and cancer of the testes or prostate are some factors males should be aware of in promoting their health.

Nocturnal Emissions

In puberty, glands in the male reproductive system begin to produce semen. To relieve the ensuing buildup of pressure, males sometimes have ejaculations while they sleep. These nocturnal emissions may be accompanied by a dream with sexual content. These emissions are also called "wet dreams" and are perfectly normal.

Hernia Problems

A hernia occurs when an internal organ pushes through the wall of muscle that normally holds it in. A common hernia in males is the inguinal hernia. Straining abdominal muscles during activities such as heavy lifting can sometimes cause tears that allow part of the intestine to push through the abdominal wall into the scrotum.

Sterility and STDs

Sterility is the inability to produce offspring. The sperm may be weak, deformed, sparse, or nonexistent. Causes of sterility can include:

- Overheating of the testes
- Exposure to certain chemicals
- Contracting mumps as an adult
- Problems with the epididymis, vas deferens, or urethra
- Infections caused by gonorrhea, syphilis, and genital herpes that damage the male reproductive system
- Complications of an untreated sexually transmitted disease (STD)
- Testicular cancer

Testicular cancer can affect a male at any age, but it occurs most often in males between the ages of 20 and 54. The main risk factor for testicular cancer is undescended testes. This condition, where one or both testes remain in the abdomen during fetal development, occurs in about three percent of boys. Surgery can correct the problem. The first sign of testicular cancer is usually a lump or the enlargement of a testis. If testicular cancer is found early, the cure rate is very high. Monthly testicular self-examination is important for early detection.

Prostate Cancer

The prostate can become enlarged as a result of a tumor. After lung cancer, prostate cancer is the most common cancer in men. Prostate cancer in boys and young men is rare, and a urinary infection or an STD can produce similar symptoms. Symptoms of prostate cancer include:

- Frequent or difficult urination

Males need to wear proper protective gear during sports to protect the reproductive organs from serious injury.

Early detection of testicular cancer can be accomplished with a simple three-minute monthly self-examination. **When is it best to conduct a monthly self-examination?**

The Male Reproductive System

Critical Thinking

Risks of STDs Discuss with students the risks of STDs to the male reproductive system. Have students work in groups and investigate descriptions, symptoms, and treatment of one STD. OL

Active Learning

Research Have students find current articles about testicular and prostate cancer and their treatment. Review the articles and then allow students to share them with the class. AL

ASSESS

Reteaching Using the diagram of the male reproductive system, point out each internal and external organ. Ask students to describe the function of each organ.

Enrichment Have students research the causes of fertility problems in men. Have them find articles about typical treatments for each of these problems and report their findings to the class.

Sum up the lesson by asking students why it is important for males to practice good personal hygiene and care for the health of the male reproductive system. In the next lesson they will learn about the female reproductive system.

What is testicular trauma?
Testicular trauma is a painful sensation males experience when the testes are struck, hit, kicked, or crushed, often during sports. Symptoms may include pain, nausea, light-headedness, dizziness, and sweating. If the pain lasts for more than an hour, or if it is accompanied by extreme swelling or discoloration, males should seek medical treatment immediately.

- Pain when urinating
- Blood in the urine
- Lingering pain in the back, hips, or pelvis

Male Reproductive Health

As the male progresses through puberty and into adulthood, regular medical exams, proper care, and personal hygiene become increasingly important.

- **Bathe Regularly.** Regular, thorough washing of the external organs is necessary. Uncircumcised males should pull the fold of the foreskin back and wash under it. A substance called smegma, which is made up of dead cells and glandular secretions, can get trapped under the foreskin and cause irritation or infection.

- **Self-Examinations.** Check the scrotum and testes monthly for signs of cancer. This is best done during or after bathing, when the skin of the scrotum is relaxed. The procedure involves gently rolling each testis between the thumb and fingers. Check for any swelling of the scrotum skin, or lumps on the side of a testis. If there are any hard lumps or nodules on a testis, or if a change in size, shape, or consistency is noted, professional medical attention is necessary. A lump doesn't necessarily mean cancer is present. Only a doctor can determine if a testicular concern is the result of an infection, a possible cancer, or an unrecognized normal structure such as a blood vessel or duct.

Lesson 1 Review

Facts and Vocabulary

1. Define the terms *scrotum* and *testes* and explain how these parts of the male reproductive system function.

2. List the external and internal male reproductive organs.

3. Analyze the relationship between good personal hygiene, health promotion, and disease prevention. Describe two ways to care for the male reproductive system.

4. Name one disorder of the male reproductive system. Explain why it is important to look for warning signs and seek early detection to prevent disease.

Thinking Critically

5. **Synthesize.** Describe the route of sperm from the testes to the penis.

6. **Evaluate.** How might the male reproductive system be affected if the reproductive glands did not function properly?

Applying Health Skills

7. **Accessing Information.** Using library resources or the Internet, identify one STD and determine how it affects the male reproductive system. Research the symptoms, diagnosis, risks, treatment, and prevention of the disease. Write a paragraph discussing why abstinence from sexual activity is the only 100 percent effective method in the prevention of STDs, including HIV/AIDS. Identify your sources, and explain why you believe they are reliable and accurate.

32 The Reproductive System

Lesson 1 Review Answers

1. The scrotum is a loose sac of skin that hangs outside the body. It holds the testes. The testes are the male sex glands, and they manufacture testosterone and produce sperm. To produce sperm, the temperature of the testes must be a few degrees lower than normal body temperature. The scrotum keeps the testes at the right temperature by holding the testes away from or close to the body as needed.

2. The external organs are the scrotum, testes, and penis. The internal organs are the vas deferens, the seminal vesicles, the prostate gland, Cowper's glands, and the urethra.

3. Care of the male reproductive system includes thorough washing of the external organs and monthly testicular self-examination.

4. Possible answer: Cancer of the testes can be detected through monthly testicular self-examination.

5. Sperm are produced in the seminiferous tubules. Next they move into the epididymis, where they mature. From the epididymis, sperm travel into the vas deferens. The vas deferens loops over the pubic bone, around the bladder, and through the prostate gland. As it passes through the prostate gland, it narrows and becomes the ejaculatory duct, which opens into the urethra. The urethra carries semen out of the body through the tip of the penis.

6. Possible answers: If the seminal vesicles did not function properly, the sperm would not receive nourishment and be mobile. If the prostate gland did not function properly, acids in the urethra and those encountered during intercourse in the vagina would destroy the sperm. If the Cowper's glands did not function properly, the acidity of any urine that might be in the urethra would destroy the sperm.

7. Answers will vary, but students might research chlamydia, gonorrhea, or human papillomavirus.

The Female Reproductive System

BIG IDEA The female reproductive system matures during puberty, and can then create new life.

QUICK WRITE

List three facts and three myths you know about the menstrual cycle. Then place a question mark next to each fact that you are unsure about or would like to understand better.

External Female Reproductive Organs

The reproductive system is the system in the body that has different organs for males and females. The female reproductive system functions to produce mature ova, or **egg cells**. An egg cell, when united with a sperm cell, forms a fertilized ovum that can develop into a new human being.

Although most of the female reproductive organs are internal, there are some external female reproductive organs. They consist of the mons pubis, labia majora (outer lips), labia minora (inner lips), vaginal opening, and clitoris. Collectively, these external organs are known as the **vulva**.

The Mons Pubis and Labia

The mons pubis is a rounded mound of fatty tissue located on the front of the female body, directly over the pubic bone. The labia majora are the fatty outer folds on either side of the vaginal opening. They make up the outer borders of the vulva. Oil and sweat glands on the inner surface of the labia majora provide moisture and lubrication.

Located between the labia majora are two smaller folds of skin known as the labia minora, which contain oil glands and blood vessels. The labia minora also contain many nerve endings and are highly sensitive. The labia serve as a line of protection against pathogens entering the body and also function in sexual arousal. The combined labia majora and labia minora surround the vaginal and urethral openings.

The Vaginal Opening

The vaginal opening lies between the labia minora and may be partially blocked by a thin membrane called the hymen. The hymen usually has several openings in it, allowing for the passage of menstrual flow. The membrane may tear during a variety of physical activities.

BEFORE YOU READ

Organize Information. Create a graphic organizer listing the external and internal female reproductive organs.

Vocabulary

egg cells
vulva
vagina
cervix
uterus
fallopian tubes
ovaries
ovulation
menstruation

The Female Reproductive System **33**

LESSON 2
The Female Reproductive System

FOCUS

BIG IDEA The female reproductive system matures during puberty and can then create new life.

Tell students that in this lesson, they will learn about the parts of the female reproductive system and the function of each part.

Reading Strategy

Organize Information Students' graphic organizers should include enough details to show that they understand the internal and external structure of the female reproductive system.

QUICKWRITE

Before students answer, write the following on the board for students to answer: *How is the female reproductive system different from the male reproductive system?* **Accept reasonable responses.**

Student Objectives

- Describe the functioning of the female reproductive system.
- Recognize the importance of early detection in the treatment of conditions involving the female reproductive system.
- Analyze the relationship between good personal hygiene and disease prevention.

TEACH

Critical Thinking

Discuss Guide students in discussing the benefits of practicing abstinence to promote the health of the reproductive system. OL

Reading Strategy

Building Vocabulary Have students look at the vocabulary words for this lesson. Then ask students which word comes from the Latin word *mensis,* meaning "month." **menstruation** OL BL EL

The Female Reproductive System

Reading Strategy

Emphasize Tell students that the mucous membrane that lines the vagina helps protect delicate vaginal tissues from injury and infection. OL

Discussing Point out that it is important during puberty to learn to care for your reproductive system. For females, this includes practicing good personal hygiene and performing monthly breast self-examinations. It also means having annual pelvic examinations by a health care professional after the age of 18 or earlier if one is sexually active. OL

Active Learning

Class Activity Refer students to the illustration of the female reproductive system. Pronounce the name of each organ in the system. Review the function of each organ. Points to emphasize include the following: 1) Unlike males, there are two openings in the female genital area. One opening is the urethra, which leads to the bladder. Urine is stored in the bladder and leaves the body through the urethra. This is part of the excretory system and has nothing to do with the reproductive system in females. 2) The other opening is the vagina, which is part of the reproductive system. A common misconception is that if a female urinates after intercourse, she will rinse out sperm and not get pregnant. Ask students why this is incorrect. **Urine leaves the body through the urethra; sperm enters through the vagina.** OL

Caption Answer: *Answers may vary but could include parents or guardians, or government or academic websites.*

Medical professionals can answer questions about reproductive health. **Who would be another good source of information?**

Hymen tissue is flexible and may stay intact during sexual intercourse. However, sperm released at the vaginal opening can enter the vagina through openings in the hymen, which may result in fertilization and pregnancy. Also between the labia minora, just above the vaginal opening, is the urethra, through which urine is secreted.

Below the mons pubis, where the labia minora meet, is a small knob of tissue called the clitoris. The labia minora form a hood-like covering over the clitoris. The clitoris plays a major role in female sexual arousal and contains many nerve endings and blood vessels, making it highly sensitive. The clitoris becomes engorged, or filled with blood, during sexual arousal.

Internal Female Reproductive Organs

The internal organs of the female reproductive system are the vagina, uterus, fallopian tubes, and ovaries.

Vagina

The **vagina** is an elastic, muscle-lined tube that extends from the uterus to outside the body and is also called the birth canal. It is three to four inches long and is capable of stretching to allow for the birth of a baby. The vagina is the repository for semen when the male ejaculates with the penis inside the vagina during intercourse. It is possible for sperm to enter the reproductive system if the male ejaculates near the opening of the vagina.

The vagina leads to the **cervix**, or the neck of the uterus. The cervical opening is quite small. During childbirth, the cervix dilates, or opens up, to allow passage of the baby. The cervix is also the site of glands that secrete mucus to lubricate the vagina.

Uterus

The **uterus** is about the size and shape of an upside-down pear. Its primary function is to hold and nourish a developing embryo and fetus. During pregnancy, the uterus will expand to hold the growing fetus. The uterus has an inner lining called the endometrium, which provides for the attachment of the embryo.

34 The Reproductive System

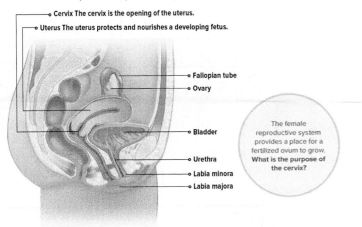

The Female Reproductive System

Cervix The cervix is the opening of the uterus.

Uterus The uterus protects and nourishes a developing fetus.

- Fallopian tube
- Ovary
- Bladder
- Urethra
- Labia minora
- Labia majora

The female reproductive system provides a place for a fertilized ovum to grow. What is the purpose of the cervix?

Fallopian Tubes

The **fallopian tubes** are tubes on each side of the uterus that connect the uterus to the region of the ovaries. They are extremely narrow and are lined with hair-like projections called cilia. Fingerlike projections at the two ends of the tubes, called fimbriae, surround the top part of the ovaries. The motions of these projections and their cilia gather a released ovum into the fallopian tube. If an ovum is present when sperm enter the fallopian tubes, fertilization may occur. Fertilization of the ovum usually occurs in the widest part of the tube, near the ovaries.

Ovaries

The **ovaries** are the two female sex glands, which produce mature ova and female hormones. They are situated on both sides of the uterus, at the open ends of the fallopian tubes. In a mature female, the ovaries release ova and produce the hormones that regulate the female reproductive cycle.

At birth, a female usually has hundreds of thousands of immature ova in her ovaries. As she enters puberty, hormones cause the ova to mature. A few hundred will mature during the reproductive years. The process of releasing one mature ovum each month into a fallopian tube is called **ovulation**. An ovum can live about a day in the fallopian tube. If sperm are present during this period, and one successfully penetrates the ovum, fertilization has occurred. Pregnancy begins at this point.

Critical Thinking

Discuss During ovulation, usually one egg is released. Fraternal twins occur when two eggs are released during ovulation and both are fertilized. Ask students how identical twins occur. OL

Reading Strategy

Emphasize The hundreds of thousands of immature ova in a female infant's ovaries are only potential sex cells. Only a few hundred cells mature and are released from the ovaries. The rest of the ova degenerate, many of them before they develop into mature ova. OL

Caption Answer: *The cervix allows passage of a baby during childbirth and is the site of glands that secrete mucus to lubricate the vagina.*

The Female Reproductive System

Reading Strategies

Explain The ovaries make estrogen and progesterone, the hormones that are primarily responsible for the changes females experience during puberty. Before puberty, estrogen and progesterone are secreted in very small amounts. OL

Caption Answer: *The lining of the uterus will support and nourish an embryo if pregnancy occurs.*

The Menstrual Cycle

Days 1–8	Days 9–13	Day 14	Days 15–28
The cycle begins with the first day of mentruation.	The hormones FSH and LH cause an egg to mature in one of the ovaries.	Ovulation occurs and the mature egg is released into one of the fallopian tubes.	The egg travels through the fallopian tube to the uterus. If the egg is not fertilized the cycle starts again.

The menstrual period occurs when an ovum is not fertilized and the lining of the uterus is shed. **What is the purpose of the uterine lining?**

The Menstrual Cycle

With each cycle, the uterus prepares for a possible pregnancy. The typical cycle is 28 days long, but it is important to know that not all females have a regular cycle. Hormones cause the uterine lining, or endometrium, to build up a thick layer of blood vessels and other tissues. This thick layer will support and nourish an embryo if pregnancy occurs.

Menstruation

If pregnancy does not occur, the uterine lining is not needed and begins to break down. The uterus contracts and the lining is shed through the vaginal opening. The process of shedding the uterine lining is called **menstruation.** Blood passing out of the body during menstruation typically amounts to about three to ten tablespoons. Because the uterus contracts as the lining is shed, the female may experience abdominal cramps during the menstrual period.

The cycle begins when the menstrual period begins. After the menstrual period ends, usually within about five days, hormones signal an ovary to release another ovum around day 14 of the cycle. The uterine lining builds up again, and if pregnancy does not occur, another menstrual period begins.

Most females begin menstruating between the ages of 11 and 15. A healthy female (who is not pregnant) will continue to menstruate fairly regularly until about age 50, when menopause occurs and menstruation ceases.

Menstrual Health Care

Good hygiene is especially important for females during the menstrual period. Daily bathing or showering is very important. If a female uses sanitary pads or panty shields to absorb the menstrual flow, she should change them every few hours. If she uses tampons—cylinders of absorbent material that are placed in the vagina—they must be changed frequently and should not be worn overnight.

Concerns About the Female Reproductive System

Although most females have a healthy reproductive system, it is important for a female to be familiar with her body and know what common problems might occur.

Menstrual Problems

- **Premenstrual Syndrome (PMS).** Some females experience premenstrual syndrome (PMS) in the week or two before their period. Symptoms can include: anxiety, depression, irritability, bloating, mood swings, and fatigue. While experts don't agree on the causes of PMS, symptoms can often be relieved by making healthful changes in one's diet and by increasing physical activity. Severe cases may be treated by a physician or nurse-practitioner with prescribed medications.

- **Dysmenorrhea.** Some females suffer from dysmenorrhea, or severe menstrual cramps. Menstrual cramps are usually mild to moderate and last only several hours. In some females, the pain may last a day or two. The pain can be controlled with over-the-counter pain medications. Light exercise or a warm bath can be helpful, as can a heating pad placed on the abdomen. In cases where severe cramping does not respond to the above actions, consultation with a medical professional is advised and prescription medication may be necessary.

- **Amenorrhea.** Amenorrhea is the term for lack of menstruation by age 16 or the stopping of menstruation in a female who previously menstruated and is not pregnant. Amenorrhea can be the result of physical defects in the reproductive organs, diseases such as diabetes, tumors, infections, anorexia, or lack of maturation of the endocrine system. Some otherwise healthy females experience amenorrhea from exercising too rigorously. An abnormally low amount of body fat accompanied by excessive exercise, sometimes experienced by professional athletes, can alter hormone levels to a point where ovulation does not occur. A female with amenorrhea should seek help from a medical professional to find the cause and correct the problem.

Female Infertility and STDs

Female infertility, the inability to become pregnant, has a variety of possible causes which include:

- The physical blocking of one or both fallopian tubes which prevents ova from passing into the uterus

- A hormonal problem causing the female to not ovulate

- Endometriosis, a condition in which endometrial (uterine lining) tissue grows outside the uterus in other areas of the pelvic cavity

- Untreated sexually transmitted diseases (STDs)

Health Minute
Strategies for Coping with PMS

If you have PMS, your symptoms might include the following:

- Bloating
- Backaches
- Sore breasts
- Depression
- Irritability

These practices can help ease the symptoms of PMS:

- Eating a balanced diet
- Limiting your caffeine intake
- Participating in regular physical activity
- Consulting your doctor or nurse-practitioner if any of these symptoms become severe

Reading Strategies

Emphasize To ease the symptoms of PMS, you can: eat a balanced diet, limit your caffeine intake, participate in regular physical activity, and consult a doctor if symptoms become severe. OL

The Female Reproductive System

Critical Thinking

Toxic-shock syndrome Toxic-shock syndrome is a condition that can cause serious illness requiring hospitalization. Have students explain how females can reduce their chances of becoming victims of toxic shock syndrome. OL

Breast Cancer Tell students that one out of every eight females living in the United States has a risk of developing breast cancer during her lifetime. Remind students that while breast cancer is the most common form of cancer in American females, it also occurs in males, though it is relatively rare (about 1 percent of all breast cancer cases). Ask students why it is important that males also learn about breast cancer. OL

Active Learning

Guest Speaker Invite a representative from the American Cancer Society to present information to the class on cervical cancer. Be sure to explain to the speaker any school guidelines regarding how much detail and what kind of information should be shared and ask to preview any audiovisual resources that will be used. OL

Problems With Infection

Several disorders can affect the female reproductive system.

- **Toxic shock syndrome (TSS).** TSS is a rare disease caused by the bacterium *Staphylococcus aureus*. Under certain conditions, the bacterium can produce a toxin that affects the immune system and the liver. Symptoms include sudden onset of fever, chills, vomiting, diarrhea, and a rash. Using high-absorbing tampons, or leaving them in too long, may create an environment in the vagina that allows production of the toxin. Tampons should be changed frequently and used with care. Some contraceptive devices, such as the diaphragm, have also been linked to TSS.

- **Vaginitis.** Vaginitis is the inflammation of vaginal tissue that results in discharge, burning, and itching. A variety of vaginal infections cause vaginitis.

- **Yeast infections.** Yeast infections are caused by a fungus and are generally characterized by a thick, white, odorless discharge accompanied by itching, burning, and painful urination. Yeast infections are rather common and should be diagnosed by a health care professional. Infections may be treated with over-the-counter medications after a definitive diagnosis.

- **Bacterial vaginosis.** This is the most common type of vaginitis that occurs during the reproductive years. The primary symptom is an odorous vaginal discharge. Trichomoniasis is a vaginal infection caused by a protozoan. Symptoms may include odorous discharge, genital itching, and painful urination. A doctor should be consulted if any of these symptoms occur, so that the organism can be identified and the infection treated.

Cancer

The most common cancers that affect the breasts and reproductive organs are breast cancer, cervical cancer, and ovarian cancer.

- Breast cancer is the most common form of cancer in American females. It is the second leading cause of death in females, after lung cancer. Two-thirds of cases occur in females older than age 50, but breast cancer can occur in younger females as well. Although it is relatively rare, males also get breast cancer. Early detection through regular medical exams and monthly self-examinations are the best defenses against breast cancer. Chances of survival are much greater when the cancer is found early. Symptoms include a change in breast or nipple appearance, a lump or swelling in the breast, or a lump in the armpit.

- Cervical cancer can be detected by getting a Pap test, which detects abnormal cells. If not caught early, cancer cells can spread to surrounding areas. There are no early symptoms of cervical cancer, but there are several risk factors: being between the ages of 20 and 30, not having regular Pap tests, having sexual intercourse at an early age, and having multiple sexual partners. All females should have a Pap test every year beginning at age 18, or earlier if they are sexually active.

- Ovarian cancer causes abnormal bleeding, unusual fatigue, unexplained weight gain or loss, and shortness of breath. Approximately 22,000 American females are diagnosed with ovarian cancer each year. More than 15,000 die from this cancer annually. The symptoms of ovarian cancer are similar to symptoms for other diseases, making it difficult to detect. They include abdominal pressure, bloating, or discomfort; nausea, indigestion, or gas; frequent urination, constipation, or diarrhea. Early detection is critical.

Female Reproductive Health

In a mature female, the cells in the lining of the vagina are constantly being shed. This often causes a slight vaginal discharge. Bathing regularly, including washing the external female reproductive organs, is an important part of good hygiene. Douches and feminine hygiene sprays are not necessary and may be irritating. Change pads or tampons often. Good personal hygiene and regular professional and self-examinations are important.

It is important to take care of your reproductive health. **How can you keep your reproductive system healthy?**

The Female Reproductive System

Reading Strategies

Emphasize Human papillomavirus (HPV) is probably the most common viral STD among sexually active young females. Infection with certain types of HPV can lead to cervical cancer. There is no known cure for HPV. OL

Emphasize Make sure that students understand that Pap tests do not test for sexually transmitted diseases. OL

Caption Answer: *Regular medical appointments, and good hygiene.*

The Female Reproductive System

Critical Thinking

Medical Exams Ask students why it is important to answer all of a physician's medical questions as truthfully as possible. Explain that the more a physician knows about a patient's medical history, the better prepared the physician is to diagnose any problems a patient might have. Encourage students to ask questions during checkups, especially during pelvic exams. The more a person asks, the better he or she understands the process. OL

Reading Strategy

Building Vocabulary A doctor who cares for the health of the female's reproductive system is called a *gynecologist*. Ask students to use a dictionary to explain the difference between a gynecologist and an obstetrician. OL

Emphasize Up to 60 percent of females experience changes in breast tissue called fibrocystic condition, in which small cysts or lumps are present in the breasts. Although fibrocystic condition is not cancerous, any female who finds a breast lump should have an examination by a doctor. OL

Caption Answer: *every month*

Pelvic Examination

The American Cancer Society recommends that females start yearly pelvic examinations three years after they become sexually active, or by age 21 at the latest. Before a pelvic exam, the physician and patient often discuss the patient's general health. Then, routine checking of blood pressure, heart rate, and lungs may be done. Urine and blood samples are usually taken.

During the actual examination, the breasts and abdomen are checked for lumps. The physician checks the external genitalia for general structure and tissue health, then performs an examination of the vagina. To help hold the walls of the vagina apart, an instrument called a speculum is inserted into the vagina. This should be a painless procedure, but because the vaginal muscles are strong, being tense may cause some discomfort. With the speculum in place, the physician collects cells from the cervix for a Pap test. This usually completes the examination.

Breast Self-Examination

Females should perform a breast self-exam (BSE) every month. The best time is right after the menstrual period, when breasts are not tender or swollen. After age 40, an annual mammogram—a series of X-rays of the breasts—is recommended in addition to the BSE.

Early detection of breast cancer can be accomplished with a simple monthly self-examination. **How often should females perform a breast self-exam?**

- While taking a shower or bath, gently explore both breast and underarm areas with your fingertips. Check the upper and outer parts of each breast, moving toward the armpit.

- Stand in front of a mirror. Check for changes in size, shape, and contour of each breast. Check for redness, swelling, or changes in the nipple.

- Lie down with one arm tucked behind the head. With the other hand, examine the opposite breast for lumps, thickening, or other changes. Move your fingers around the breast in a circle, then up and down, covering the entire breast area. Repeat on the other breast.

Lesson 2 Review

Facts and Vocabulary

1. Define the terms *cervix* and *uterus* and explain how these parts of the female reproductive system function.

2. List the external and internal female reproductive organs.

3. Name two disorders of the female reproductive system. Explain why it is important to look for warning signs and seek early detection to prevent disease.

4. Analyze the importance of good personal hygiene for disease prevention. Describe three ways to care for the female reproductive system.

Thinking Critically

5. **Synthesize.** How might you respond if a friend told you she always experiences discomfort the week before her menstrual period?

6. **Analyze.** A female who is experiencing symptoms of vaginitis goes to see her doctor. Write a paragraph that suggests how the doctor might be able to distinguish among these possible conditions: a yeast infection, bacterial vaginosis, and trichomoniasis.

Applying Health Skills

7. **Advocacy.** A favorite cousin of yours, who is 22 years old, tells you she has never had a Pap test. She says that seeing a doctor and getting a Pap test aren't important until females are much older. Write your cousin a letter in which you explain what you have learned about regular health care for the female reproductive system.

The Female Reproductive System **41**

LESSON 2
The Female Reproductive System

REAL WORLD CONNECTION

Breast Cancer Statistics Encourage students to examine the webpage provided to verify the elements of a valid source of information. Have them check the site's sponsor, verify additional links, and identify citations from specific sources. Ask students to summarize the reliability of this resource in a paragraph.

ASSESS

Reteaching Using the diagram of the female reproductive system, point out each internal and external organ. Ask students to name and describe the functions of each organ.

Enrichment Have students research various methods of alleviating the pain of abdominal cramps early in the menstrual period. Ask students which methods they think will work best and why.

Sum up the lesson by asking students the three most important things they learned in this lesson. Emphasize how important it is for females to keep themselves and their reproductive systems healthy.

Lesson 2 Review Answers

1. The cervix is the neck of the uterus. The uterus is a hollow, muscular organ that receives and holds the fertilized ovum during pregnancy. The primary function of the uterus is to hold and nourish a developing embryo and fetus. The cervix has a very small opening that dilates, or opens up, to allow a baby to pass out of the uterus during birth.

2. The external organs are the mons pubis, labia majora, labia minora, vaginal opening, and clitoris. The internal organs are the vagina, uterus, fallopian tubes, and ovaries.

3. Two possible disorders are breast cancer and cervical cancer. Breast cancer can be detected through monthly self-examination and also through annual mammograms, which are recommended for all women after age 40. Cervical cancer can be detected by getting an annual Pap test.

4. Care of the female reproductive system includes good personal hygiene, monthly breast self-exams, and regular examinations by a physician, including a Pap test after age 18 or earlier if sexually active.

5. The friend is experiencing PMS. Students should include strategies for reducing discomfort, including eating a good diet, and increasing physical activity.

6. Paragraphs will vary. But should mention finding out if there is an odorless or odorous discharge and testing in some way to identify the responsible organism.

7. Letters will vary, but students should note that a Pap test can detect cervical cancer in the early stages, which is easier to treat than in later stages, and that risk factors for cervical cancer include being between the ages of 20 and 30 and not having regular Pap tests. Letters should present the student's case convincingly.

Hormones and Sexual Feelings

FOCUS

BIG IDEA Sexual feelings are a result of hormones and are normal and healthy.

Explain that when in an emotional state such as sexual excitement, it may be easy to be overwhelmed by such feelings and more difficult to make a responsible decision. Students should recognize that having predetermined limits will help them stick to their responsible choices during stressful times.

Reading Strategy

Predict Students' paragraphs will vary.

QUICKWRITE

> Before students answer, write the following on the board for students to answer: *Why is it important to set personal limits on sexual behavior before getting involved in a situation where sexual feelings are present?*

Student Objectives

- Examine the effect of hormones on body systems.
- Demonstrate healthful decision-making skills that show responsible behavior for your health and the health of others.

TEACH

Health Skills Practice

Goal Setting Help students understand that setting goals is a sign of maturity and can enhance a person's ability to make mature, responsible decisions. OL

Critical Thinking

Discussing Ask students to discuss the difference between love and sexual excitement. Emphasize that love is an emotional feeling, while sexual excitement is an automatic physiological response. Explain that some people may confuse the two, but that it is important to remember that sexual excitement is a result of hormones being released. OL

Hormones and Sexual Feelings

BEFORE YOU READ

Predict. Write a brief paragraph describing what information you believe this lesson will contain.

Vocabulary
hormones

BIG IDEA Sexual feelings are a result of hormones and are normal and healthy.

QUICK WRITE

On a sheet of paper, list as many physical changes or reactions as you can think of that are caused by hormones.

Sexual Feelings and Response

Sexual feelings are normal and healthy, and they are controlled by the same **hormones** that affect your physical growth. Hormones are chemical substances produced in glands, which regulate the activities of different body cells and organs. Biologically speaking, sexual feelings are essential for the reproductive process.

Sex hormones cause the body to respond to sexual stimulation, which may result from a kiss, holding hands, or thinking about a date. Physical responses to excitement in males and females may include:

- Increased heart rate
- Faster breathing
- Clammy hands
- Flushed face
- Erection of the penis in males
- Production of vaginal fluids in females

These responses are natural and people cannot keep them from occurring. However, a person must decide what to do about them. It is a good idea to establish predetermined limits on sexual behavior and stop things before they start. Establishing limits shows that you accept responsibility for your sexual health and your future.

Sexual Feelings and Responsible Decisions

Physical feelings can sometimes be confused for emotional feelings, such as love. Remember, hormones cause sexual feelings, and sexual feelings are a normal physical response. You have complete control over what you do about these feelings. When they occur, the important thing is to make healthful and responsible decisions.

Responsible decisions about sexual feelings are easier to make when shared activities take place that involve lots of other people and interesting things to see and do. **What are some other benefits of group dates or double dates?**

If you feel overwhelmed by sexual feelings, remind yourself of your long-term goals. Consequences of engaging in sexual behavior may keep you from pursuing your dreams of going to college and having a career. Keeping your goals in mind will help you make mature, responsible decisions.

If you know what sexual feelings are and understand the body's physical response to them, you can make more responsible decisions concerning those feelings. Remember that your body has some urges that you cannot control. Whether you want to or not, you will sometimes feel hungry, sleepy, or sexually aroused. Just as you can control what you eat and when you sleep, you also control how you respond to sexual feelings. By controlling how you react to sexual arousal, you are taking steps toward behaving maturely and making responsible decisions that will help you to reach your goals for the future and to build a positive self-concept.

Lesson 3 Review

Facts and Vocabulary

1. What causes the body's response to sexual stimulation?

2. Name four of the body's first physiological responses to sexual stimulation.

3. Explain why it is important for a teen to establish predetermined limits on sexual behavior before he or she encounters a situation where a decision must be made.

Thinking Critically

4. **Evaluate.** Are sexual feelings and love the same thing? Explain your answer.

5. **Analyze.** Discuss how keeping your long-term goals in mind can help you make mature, responsible decisions when you experience sexual urges. How can these decisions affect your health and the health of others?

Applying Health Skills

6. **Goal Setting.** Identify one of your long-term goals. Describe a concept for a cartoon strip in which your focus on this goal helps you and a date choose an activity that you can enjoy together without placing yourself in a sexual situation.

Hormones and Sexual Feelings **43**

Lesson 3 Review Answers

1. Sex hormones cause the body to respond to sexual stimulation.

2. Answers may include any four of the following: the heart rate increases, breathing speeds up, hands feel clammy, the face gets flushed, the penis swells, the vaginal walls swell, the vagina becomes lubricated, the clitoris swells.

3. Once sexual tension builds up, it is more difficult to make a responsible decision.

4. Sexual feelings are not the same as love. Sexual feelings are triggered by hormones. Love is a deep *emotional* bond, not an automatic response.

5. Answers will vary, but students may note that thinking about something they really want in the future can motivate them to plan ahead.

6. Cartoons will vary. But should demonstrate an understanding that the goal provides a positive influence on decisions.

Denis Raev/iStock/360/Getty Images

Hormones and Sexual Feelings

Reading Strategy

Building Vocabulary Write the term *hormones* on the board. Have volunteers recall the definition from a previous lesson. Then have students look up the word in the Glossary/Glosario. OL BL EL

Active Learning

Class Activity Have students consider the relationship between how a person chooses to respond to sexual feelings and the effects of that response on a person's long-term goals. Ask volunteers to give examples of how responsible decisions regarding sexual activity can be made by keeping goals in mind. OL

Critical Thinking

Discussing Have students discuss the following statement: *A couple can have a long-lasting relationship that does not include sexual intercourse.* OL

Caption Answer: *Other benefits of group or double dates might include feeling safer in a group and sharing costs with more people.*

ASSESS

Reteaching Explain that we cannot keep our hormones from causing sexual feelings. Emphasize, however, that while we have no control over the hormones, we have control over how we react to those feelings and are able to make responsible decisions about them.

Enrichment Have students research the hormones affecting the autonomic nervous system, the system that helps maintain the body's metabolism. Have them present a report or prepare a video to share this information with the rest of the class.

Sum up the lesson by telling students that this lesson is intended to support young people in making responsible decisions about sexual activity.

MODULE 3
Assessment Answers

1. The epididymis is a highly coiled structure located on the back side of each testis. Over a period of 64 days, sperm produced in each testis mature in the epididymis.

2. The urethra.

3. Semen is made up of sperm and secretions from the testes, secretions from the seminal vesicles that nourish sperm and help make them mobile, secretions from the prostate that neutralize acids in the urethra and the vagina, and secretions from Cowper's glands that lubricate the urethra and neutralize acidity of any urine that is present.

4. Activities such as heavy lifting can result in inguinal hernia.

5. The fallopian tubes are tubes on each side of the uterus that connect the uterus to the region of the ovaries. When an ovum is released from an ovary, motions of the fingerlike projections at the end of the tube near the ovary draw the ovum into the tube. Fertilization usually occurs in the widest part of the tube.

6. Menstruation usually begins between the ages of 10 and 15.

7. For males, any three: overheating of the testes, exposure to certain chemicals, contracting mumps as an adult, an untreated STD, and problems with the epididymis, vas deferens, or urethra. For females, any three: physical blocking of one or both fallopian tubes, failure to ovulate (usually for hormonal reasons), endometriosis, and untreated STDs.

8. Symptoms include a change in breast or nipple appearance, a lump or swelling in the breast, and a lump in the armpit.

9. Answers will vary, but students should discuss the importance of cleanliness, care in lifting heavy objects, self-exams for males and females, regular physical exams, and seeing a health care professional when a possible problem occurs.

10. Forty-six chromosomes are needed—23 from the male's sperm and 23 from the female's ovum.

11. It is the only body system that is different for males and females.

12. Ovulation must occur before fertilization can take place. Menstruation does not occur if fertilization has taken place.

13. Dialogues will vary, but students should point out that vaginal infections are fairly common and could have many causes, some of which require prescribed medication.

14. Answers will vary, but students should demonstrate a caring attitude and should explain that changes during the teen years are normal and what this means in terms of their sibling's maturing body.

Reviewing Facts and Vocabulary

1. Describe the structure and function of the epididymis.

2. What is the duct that travels through the penis?

3. Describe the composition of semen.

4. What type of movement can cause an inguinal hernia?

5. What are the fallopian tubes, and what role do they play in the female reproductive system?

6. Between what ages do most females begin menstruating?

7. Name three causes of sterility in males. Name three causes of infertility in females.

8. What are three symptoms of breast cancer?

Writing Critically

9. Evaluate. Write down some important health decisions you can make to keep your reproductive system healthy.

10. Synthesize. Write a one-page summary describing the reproductive process, including how many chromosomes are combined to produce a human offspring.

11. Synthesize. Write a summary describing what is unique about the male and female reproductive systems when compared to the other systems of the body.

12. Analyze. Write a summary describing how ovulation, menstruation, and fertilization are interrelated.

Applying Health Skills

13. Advocacy. Your friend has told you that she has had an unusual vaginal discharge for several days. She is worried and afraid to tell anyone else. Write a dialogue that helps her to overcome her fears and understand how important it is to get medical care so that her condition can be properly identified and treated.

14. Communication Skills. A younger sibling of your own gender seems upset. When you ask what is wrong, he or she expresses worry about becoming a teen. Discuss with your younger sibling what to expect during puberty.

BEYOND THE CLASSROOM ACTIVITIES

PARENT INVOLVEMENT
School Nurse. Invite the school nurse into the classroom to discuss issues concerning puberty and reproductive health. Have parents attend the class session to hear the nurse's presentation. List positive ways that teens can promote their reproductive health.

SCHOOL AND COMMUNITY
Adolescent Health. Interview a health care provider who specializes in adolescent care. Describe the academic preparation necessary for that career and the personal characteristics necessary to be successful in that field.

BEYOND THE CLASSROOM

Parent Involvement: School Nurse. Invite the school nurse into the classroom to discuss issues concerning puberty and reproductive health. Have parents attend the class session to hear the nurse's presentation. List the positive ways that teens can promote their reproductive health.

School and Community: Adolescent Health. Have students interview a health care provider who specializes in adolescent care. Then have them describe the academic preparation necessary for that career and the personal characteristics necessary to be successful in that field.

- Encourage parents to meet with the school nurse during or before the classroom visit. Issues to discuss may include dating, peer pressure, abstinence, sexually transmitted diseases (including HIV infection), and pressure to use drugs and alcohol.

- Answers will vary but should indicate that students recognize the range and depth of training and personal qualifications needed for the profession.

MODULE 4	STANDARDS / NOTES ✎	LESSON ASSESSMENT
	Use this space for standards and notes.	Module 4 Assessment Online assessment
30 MIN. **LESSON 1** **The Commitment to Marry** **BIG IDEA.** There are many challenges related to the commitment of marriage.		Lesson 1 Review Online assessment
30 MIN. **LESSON 2** **Becoming a Parent** **BIG IDEA.** Parenthood and raising a family requires a great amount of responsibility.		Lesson 2 Review Online assessment

Key to Abilities   Teaching Strategies and Activities have been coded for ability level and appropriateness.

AL Activities for students working above grade level

BL Activities for students working below grade level

OL Activities for students working on grade level

EL Activities for English Learners

Marriage and Parenthood

Module Overview Module 4 focuses on the transition of dating relationships into marital relationships and discusses the role parents must play in the development of their children's health.

LESSON 1
Distinguish the differences between a dating relationship and a marital relationship and demonstrate how couples use effective communication skills in building and maintaining healthy relationships.

LESSON 2
Evaluate the effects of family relationships on physical, mental/emotional, and social health and describe the roles and responsibilities of parents.

Activating Prior Knowledge

Using Visuals Have students look at the picture on this page and explain that mature, caring adults make good parents.

Ask Students: *Write three specific responsibilities parents have for their children.*

The Commitment to Marry

FOCUS

BIG IDEA There are many challenges related to the commitment of marriage.

Reading Strategy

Explain Students' answers will vary.

QUICKWRITE

After students answer, write the following on the board for students to answer: *Do you plan to get married? If so, at what age do you think you will marry?* **Write the number of students who plan to marry on the board. Then write the ages at which these people indicated they think they will marry. Have students calculate the average ages for each gender. Compare the figures for your class with the following statistic: The average age for first marriages in the United States is about 27 for males and 25 for females.**

Student Objectives

- Distinguish between a dating relationship and marital relationship.
- Demonstrate how couples use effective communication skills in building and maintaining healthy relationships.
- Describe the effects of divorce on adults.

TEACH

Critical Thinking

Reasons to Marry Ask students to create a list of reasons why two adults might marry. Have students explain why it is important for a person to be mentally and emotionally mature before entering into a marriage. Ask students to think about how people come to love one another. Ask them why this often leads to marriage. OL

Caption Answer: *They can talk about their reasons for marrying and any doubts they may have about their commitment to each other.*

The Commitment to Marry

BEFORE YOU READ

Explain. Write a short summary explaining what you think the commitment to marry means. How does committing to marriage change a relationship?

Vocabulary
commitment
blended family

BIG IDEA There are many challenges related to the commitment of marriage.

QUICK WRITE

Imagine that your boyfriend or girlfriend has proposed marriage to you. *Write a letter to him or her explaining why you are not ready for marriage.*

Marriage: A Lifelong Commitment

Many people choose to marry during their lifetime. Practicing healthful behaviors in dating relationships can help individuals prepare for the responsibility of marriage. A marriage is different from a dating relationship in many ways. First, people who enter a marriage make a lifelong **commitment** to someone they love. A commitment is a promise or a pledge. In addition, in order for a marriage to be successful, both partners must be ready for new responsibilities and challenges that do not exist in a dating relationship. In order to determine whether they are ready for the commitment of marriage, couples need to honestly evaluate themselves, including their goals for the future and for their relationships.

Marriage allows couples to share their lives together in an intimate, mature way. It also provides companionship in both good and hard times, in adulthood and into later life.

People can marry for reasons other than the intention of committing to a future with someone they love. It is important for both people in a relationship to closely examine their reasons for marrying and to discuss any doubts they may have about their commitment to each other. These discussions should take place before a couple gets married to reduce the possibility of conflict. They will have a better chance at a successful marriage if they seriously consider how well they know each other and if they discuss their goals and expectations for their new life together.

Marriage is a life-changing commitment that requires maturity from both partners. **What can couples do to achieve their goals for the future?**

46 Marriage and Parenthood

Adjusting to Marriage

Making a commitment to another person is just the beginning of a successful marriage. Couples can become caught up in the excitement of planning a wedding, choosing a place to live together, and sharing their plans with friends and family. Therefore, they may pay less attention to preparing themselves for the transition to becoming a married couple. In the early stages of the marriage, couples will face adjustments, such as sharing living quarters, finances, and families. During this adjustment period, the emotional and social maturity of both partners is crucial to the success of marriage.

In a marriage, a person understands their own needs as well as their partner's needs, and they know how to meet those needs in healthy ways. They compromise and make sacrifices in order to make their marriage successful. Couples understand that they will face difficulties in life and are committed to working through these difficulties together. Even when conflicts between couples arise, they face these challenges with good communication and compassion.

Sociologists have identified a number of factors associated with a successful marriage. In general, couples should:

- Agree on important issues in their relationship.
- Share common interests and values.
- Demonstrate affection and share confidences.
- Show a willingness to compromise and put others first.
- Share similarities in family backgrounds.
- Have parents who had a successful marriage.
- Not have major conflicts with their in-laws.
- Have several good friends of both genders.
- Have had a long period of close association prior to marriage.
- Have stable jobs and career goals.
- Agree on how they feel about raising children.

Partners with many of these characteristics have an increased chance of building a lasting, happy marriage.

When marriage partners share common interests and activities, their marriage becomes stronger. **Think of a married couple you know. How do they enjoy their time together?**

LESSON 1
The Commitment to Marry

Critical Thinking

Discuss Have students discuss how long they think a couple should know each other before considering marriage. OL

Reading Strategy

Building Vocabulary Tell students that the word commitment comes from the Latin word *committere,* which means "to connect" or "to entrust." Ask students how these word origins relate to the commitment of marriage. **In a marriage, you share a special connection with another person, whom you have entrusted to share your life with you.** OL **EL**

Critical Thinking

Understanding Needs Ask students: *Why is it important to understand your own needs? How can understanding one's needs contribute to the success of marriage?* OL

Caption Answer: *Students' answers will vary.*

The Commitment to Marry

Reading Strategy

Emphasize Remind students that when a couple divorces, it does not change the love that the parents have for their children. Children whose parents have divorced need to know that it is okay to love both parents and that it's normal to feel sad, angry, and/or depressed. Talking about their feelings helps young people adjust to the changes in their lives and to accept that their parents' marriage is over. OL

Caption Answer: *Talking openly about the situation can ease stress.*

Joint custody may be challenging, but it allows both parents to remain involved in their children's lives. **What healthful behaviors can help family members adjust to a divorce?**

Seeking help from a professional counselor can help families resolve difficult problems. Even if divorce occurs, counseling can help all family members adjust to the change.

Marriage and Divorce

There were more than 700,000 divorces on record in the United States during 2019. Although this number is high, divorce rates have been decreasing steadily since 2001. Divorce can be devastating to children. The family physically separates, and one parent moves out of the home, sometimes to a distant location. Children may feel sad about not growing up with both parents under the same roof. Sometimes children may have to move, which can mean changing schools and leaving friends behind. In addition, families may have to adjust to a lower standard of living because the income is split between two homes. Divorce puts a strain on the entire family and may also impact relationships between individual family members.

In cases where spousal or child abuse is involved, divorce can be a necessary, positive change. It is critical that victims of abuse leave the unsafe environment. Even in situations where there is no physical abuse, emotional turmoil in the household may create an unhealthy atmosphere for family members. This type of environment can have a permanently negative effect on a child's ability to form healthy relationships later in life. In such cases, divorce may be an appropriate step so that family members can build a new, healthier life.

Although divorce is an adult problem, children may blame themselves for what went wrong and not understand that the divorce had nothing to do with their own behaviors. Because divorce affects children so strongly, it is essential that parents explore all options, including couples counseling, before making the decision to end the marriage. Above all, both partners should remain responsible parents when making these important decisions.

Joint Custody

Sometimes divorced couples have joint custody of their children, meaning that the children spend time living with each parent. Depending on work and other schedules, a child may be with one parent during the week and the other parent on weekends, or children may live with one parent for six months of the year and with the other parent for the rest of the year. Joint custody can be challenging to children. However, it also allows both parents to remain involved and to give their children the necessary guidance and support.

Blended Families

People who get divorced may choose to remarry, and it is common for a new spouse to bring his or her own children into the new marriage. This creates a **blended family**. The new couple may also adopt or have children together in addition to their previous children.

48 Marriage and Parenthood

Children may experience stress as they adjust to new relationships in the blended family. They may feel resentful of their stepparent or jealous of new stepsiblings. If the stepparent and other children have moved into the child's home, the child may resent having to share it with others. The child may also struggle to get his or her own parent's attention. Emotions such as anger, jealousy, and sadness are normal. To help them adjust to changes after a remarriage, children should be encouraged to talk to their parents, relatives, teachers, counselors, or other trusted adults.

Teen Marriage

Because a successful marriage requires both people to be responsible and mature, the odds are not in favor of people who marry in their teens. There are good reasons for teens to delay marriage until they are more mature:

- Married teens have to focus on their marriage and may not have the time or energy to work on their own personal growth and development.
- Married teens may have to postpone college, job training, or beginning a career. With limited earning power, financial difficulties can arise and threaten the marriage.
- If the teen couple married because of a pregnancy, the emotional and financial stresses on the relationship can be even more severe.

Character Check

If someone you know is going through a difficult divorce, show your compassion and empathy by being available to listen. Make a list of actions you might take to show your friend that you care.

Lesson 1 Review

Facts and Vocabulary

1. Define the term *commitment*. How is commitment to a marriage different from commitment to a dating relationship?

2. Explain how a mature couple handles conflict. How does this demonstrate the use of communication skills in building and maintaining healthy relationships?

3. What is a blended family?

4. How does making the decision to delay marriage until they are more mature help teens to promote individual and family health?

Thinking Critically

5. **Analyze.** Describe some characteristics that indicate a couple is ready for marriage. Explain how these characteristics enhance the dignity, respect, and responsibility required in a healthy marriage.

6. **Synthesize.** Make a list of ways that divorce can affect children and some healthful ways to deal with divorce.

Applying Health Skills

7. **Analyzing Influences.** Briefly describe a family sitcom or drama on television. Does the show portray relationships between married couples and their children realistically? How do you think media representations of marriage and family relationships influence viewers?

The Commitment to Marry **49**

LESSON 1
The Commitment to Marry

Active Learning

Class Activity Have students compile a list of television shows that depict divorced or blended families. Have them discuss some of the problems experienced by the parents and children in those families. AL

Critical Thinking

Blended Families Have students suggest strategies for getting to know new stepparents and stepsiblings. OL

Teen Marriage Ask students to list what they would like to accomplish in their lives and how marrying in their teens might affect their ability to achieve these goals. Have students discuss the reasons why most teen marriages do not last. Then discuss problems that occur in teen marriages. **Responses may include a desire to go to college, wanting the freedom to go out with their friends when they want to, and not wanting to be tied down.** OL

ASSESS

Reteaching Have students review the list of reasons why teens should delay marriage. Remind students that marriage takes a great deal of work and patience.

Enrichment Have students collect the age data on divorce rates for different states. Ask whether their findings support the correlation between early marriage and divorce.

Sum up the lesson by telling students that successful marriages occur when two people are mentally and emotionally mature and are willing to work through their problems together.

Lesson 1 Review Answers

1. A commitment is a promise or a pledge. Answers will vary, but should include a readiness to take on responsibilities.

2. The couple faces these challenges and demonstrates communication and compassion.

3. A blended family is a family where two adults marry and have children from a previous marriage living with them.

4. Marrying young may force a teen to postpone college, job training, or beginning a career; marrying young because of pregnancy places emotional and financial stresses on the relationship.

5. Students should discuss how maturity, commitment, and mutual love and respect contribute to a healthy marriage.

6. Possible negative effects of divorce may include: one parent moving out, facing potential financial difficulties, and difficult emotions. Healthful ways to deal with divorce include keeping the lines of communication open; talking to relatives and other trusted adults.

7. Answers will vary. Students should provide specific reasons to back up their opinions.

Becoming a Parent

FOCUS

BIG IDEA Parenthood and raising a family requires a great amount of responsibility.

Reading Strategy

List Students' lists will vary.

QUICKWRITE

Before students answer, write the following on the board for students to answer: *Do you want to have children in the future? What are some reasons to have children?* On the board, write the number of students who indicated in the Motivator that they would like to have children in the future. With the class, calculate this percentage for both genders. Then have students share their reasons for wanting to be parents. Write this list on the board and have students compare this list to the reasons listed in the lesson.

Student Objectives

- Describe the roles and responsibilities of parents.
- Evaluate the effects of family relationships on physical, mental/emotional, and social health.
- Analyze the importance and benefits of abstinence

TEACH

Active Learning

Maturity Have students create a list of reasons why it is important to be both physically and emotionally mature before making the decision to become a parent. Remind students to think of both the child and the parents when creating their lists. OL

Reading Strategy

Building Vocabulary Write the following vocabulary term on the board: *parenting*. Have students write their idea of what this word means and then check the definition in the dictionary and Glossary/Glosario. OL EL

Caption Answer: *Parents provide food, shelter, and clothing.*

Becoming a Parent

BIG IDEA Parenthood and raising a family requires a great amount of responsibility.

BEFORE YOU READ

List. Describe some of the responsibilities of parenthood.

Vocabulary
heredity
parenting
single-parent family

QUICK WRITE

Make a word web to describe what you know about caring for an infant. Write the word Infant in the middle of a sheet of paper, and circle it. Around the word, write down what responsibilities come to mind. Connect these words and phrases to the center circle.

Why People Have Children

Raising children can be the most rewarding and enriching aspect of a person's life. Couples who face the many challenges of parenting feel great joy and love as they watch their children grow. Many married couples find that building a healthy, happy family together is an important, fulfilling life experience.

People give all kinds of reasons for having children, including passing on the family name and **heredity**—genetic characteristics passed from parent to child—giving one's parents a grandchild, wanting to be loved by someone, giving in to pressure from friends or parents, and bringing stability to a shaky marriage. Many parents agree the best reason for bringing a child into the world is being ready to raise a family and share the love of the marriage. A new life is a great responsibility, and love for that new life is essential.

Parental Responsibilities

Parenting means providing care, support, and love in a way that leads to a child's total development. It is one of the most important jobs a person can have. Parents must provide the child with basic physical needs: food, clothing, shelter, and medical care. In addition, parents must also meet their child's developmental and emotional needs. They can do this by ensuring that the child is loved unconditionally and receives the proper nurturing and education to succeed later in life.

Parents also need to give guidance to their children. They should help their children understand right from wrong and develop a good self-concept. By setting limits and providing guidance, parents help children become self-directed and responsible. It is important that parents provide their children a loving, safe, and supportive environment in which they can grow into responsible, healthy, happy, and independent people.

Parenting involves nurturing a child's physical, mental/emotional, and social development from infancy through adulthood. List three specific examples of responsibilities parents have toward their children.

50 Marriage and Parenthood

Parenting skills contribute to strong family relationships. Having this foundation will promote the physical, mental/emotional, and social health of all family members.

Teen Parenthood

While parenting is rewarding and full of joy, it is also demanding and full of challenges. Even some mature adults have difficulty adjusting to parenthood. The challenges to teens are even greater.

The reason many teens give for wanting a baby is to have someone who will love them. However, in the early stages of a child's development, the parent is responsible for providing for the child's every need. Therefore, parents must be ready to give love, rather than receive it. Many teens are not prepared to handle the emotional demands and responsibilities of raising a child.

Having a baby is tremendously rewarding when the child is brought into a loving, nurturing, and stable environment. However, with all the challenges of adolescence, most teens find the reality of raising a baby to be overwhelming. For most teens, having a baby is not a conscious decision; 67 percent of teen pregnancies are unplanned. A smaller percentage of teens plan to get pregnant, believing that having a child will solve other problems. They quickly find out that the problems have not disappeared and that they now face greater challenges.

Teen parents face many challenges. Some of those challenges include the following:

- Teens may want to escape school or home, only to find they have no support system and a poor career outlook.
- Teens may think that having a baby will strengthen their relationship with their girlfriend or boyfriend. However, if a relationship is not strong enough already, having a baby will not make it better.
- Teens may want to prove to themselves or others that they are adults, only to learn they are unprepared for many adult responsibilities.
- A female teen may want to be the focus of attention, especially while pregnant, but she soon finds the baby takes all the attention.

Impact on Physical and Mental/Emotional Health

Expectant mothers require special medical attention to ensure that they stay healthy and have a healthy baby. Regular prenatal care is essential, as is a healthful diet, adequate physical activity and rest, and a strong support network. However, teens are the least likely of all age groups to get the proper medical attention, and many times their diets do not meet the nutritional demands of a growing fetus.

In addition, teen mothers face a higher risk of medical complications. These include early or prolonged labor, high blood pressure, and anemia, a condition where the body does not produce enough red blood cells, causing fatigue and headaches. For teens younger than 15 years of age, the likelihood of complications is even greater. Babies of teen mothers are more likely to be born with health problems, including those associated with low birth weight.

One of the best ways parents can provide a nurturing environment for their children is to spend time with them. **How do parenting skills contribute to strong family relationships?**

Becoming a Parent

Reading Strategy

Emphasize It is important that teens understand that parents make many adjustments to their lives when they have a child. Ask students to think about what sort of changes new parents make. OL

Critical Thinking

Supportive Environment Ask students to think about what parents do to give their children a safe, supportive environment. Ask them why it might be difficult for teen parents to do the same for a child. OL

Active Learning

Guest Speaker Invite a parenting instructor to speak to your class about the responsibilities and tasks involved in raising children. OL

Caption Answer: *Parenting skills promote the physical, mental/emotional, and social health of all family member.*

Becoming a Parent

Reading Strategy

Emphasize Teens sometimes have children to fulfill emotional needs. A teen who feels he or she wants to have a baby should discuss this issue with a trusted adult, to explore other ways to meet such needs. OL

Critical Thinking

Social Consequences Ask students to discuss the social consequences of teen parenthood. Ask students to discuss how their social lives would be affected by having a child. What would be the impact on a teen's family if he or she became a parent? OL

Caption Answer (top): *Demands of caring for a child would make it difficult to spend time with friends.*

Caption Answer (bottom): *Teens have not yet met educational goals, are not financially prepared to raise a child, and are not yet ready to care for the developmental needs of a child.*

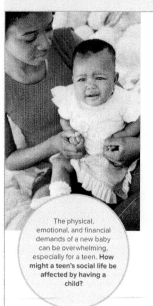

The physical, emotional, and financial demands of a new baby can be overwhelming, especially for a teen. **How might a teen's social life be affected by having a child?**

Couples who choose to remain abstinent can focus on their goals and dreams for the future. **What are three reasons to delay parenthood until a teen is mature and in a committed relationship?**

For many mature adult females, pregnancy can be a joyous, exciting time but also an emotionally stressful one. For a pregnant teen, the stress can become overwhelming because she often does not have the maturity or support she needs. Pregnancy is the most common reason teens drop out of school.

Impact on Social Life

Having a baby makes it very challenging for teens to have an active social life. The around-the-clock demands of a baby make it hard for teen parents to find time and healthy ways to meet their emotional needs. New parents find that their social activities become limited because of their new responsibilities. They often have to juggle difficult schedules and cannot spend as much time with friends and family as they once did. Being away from friends and the lack of preparation for the parental role can leave teen parents feeling frustrated and depressed.

Single Teen Parents

Most female teens who become pregnant do not marry the father of their baby. Even if a teen couple marries, staying married will be difficult. Most babies of teen parents are raised in a **single-parent family**.

Life for single teen mothers can be full of risks and challenges. Apart from being less likely to finish high school, teen mothers are more likely to be dependent on others for financial support, more likely to earn a lower income, and may be unable to lead the life of a normal teen.

To cope with some of these problems, many single teenage mothers live with their parents. Some parents help with childcare and provide the financial assistance, love, and support needed by both the mother and her infant. Many states require a teen parent to live with her parents if she is receiving financial aid from the government. If the parents are supportive, living at home is probably the best solution for the teen parents and the child.

Single teen fathers also face difficulties. They are often not mature enough to provide the child with the necessary care, nurturing, and guidance. In addition, most states require a teen father to provide financial support for his child. He may then have to quit school to get a job. Without a high school diploma, however, he may always have difficulty getting a well-paying job, and college might be beyond reach. Both his emotional and social health may also suffer as a result.

Deciding on Teen Parenthood

For teens, the decision to delay parenthood until they are more mature and in a committed relationship provides the best opportunity for a happy future. Teens need to discuss goals and feelings about the future, and then decide whether they are ready for marriage or children.

In a healthy, loving relationship, teen couples support each other's future goals. They can be responsible and realistic when making the decision to become a parent, or wait until they are older before having a child. Mature, responsible teens also recognize that only abstinence offers complete protection against pregnancy. When teens choose to remain abstinent, they are protecting their health and their future.

Before deciding to become a parent, it is important to ask the following questions:

1. What are your goals for the next two years? Five years? Ten years?
2. How will a child change my goals?
3. What are your reasons for becoming a parent?
4. How will you provide financial stability for the child?
5. In what ways will you provide guidance, instill values, and set limits to your child?
6. How will you handle the personal and social restrictions a child places on your life?
7. How will you handle the educational and professional restrictions a child places on your life?
8. How will you provide the basic necessities (diapers, baby formula, clothes, medical care, shelter) for your child?
9. What are some risks your child will face being born and raised by a teen?
10. How will teen pregnancy affect the people in your family?

Lesson 2 Review

Facts and Vocabulary

1. List reasons people give for deciding to have children.
2. Explain why pregnancy presents a health risk to a teen and her baby.
3. List some of the risks and challenges for a teen father.

Thinking Critically

4. **Analyze.** Evaluate the effects of parenting and family relationships on physical, mental/emotional, and social health.
5. **Evaluate.** Describe the roles and responsibilities of parents in promoting healthy families. What you think are the two most important responsibilities of being a parent? Why?
6. **Synthesize.** What stressful situations might a teen experience as a result of an unplanned pregnancy? Why is it important for teens to practice abstinence?

Applying Health Skills

7. **Refusal Skills.** Using information on how pregnancy affects a teen's physical, mental/emotional, and social health, provide ways you could refuse engaging in sexual activity with a boyfriend or girlfriend. Write down at least two specific refusal statements.

Becoming a Parent 53

Lesson 2 Review Answers

1. They love children; They want to pass on the family name and heredity; They wish to give one's parents a grandchild; They want to be loved by someone.
2. Teens are less likely to get proper medical attention, and have a higher risk of medical complications.
3. A teen father may need to quit high school to get a job to help support the child.
4. Teen parents often depend on their families for financial and emotional support. Meeting the needs of mother and infant puts a strain on families.
5. Answers will vary, but students should mention examples of the parents' responsibility to meet the child's physical, mental, emotional, and social needs.
6. Students may suggest problems with parents, peers, and the other parent of the child.
7. Answers will vary. Refusal statements may convey the risk of complications during pregnancy, not being able to finish high school, having to give up a normal social life, or giving up goals.

Becoming a Parent

Health Skills Practice

Accessing Information Have students research more about California's Safely Surrendered Baby Law. When was the law created? **2001** Has it been successful? **There has been an 80 percent decrease in abandonment cases.** What other states have safe haven laws? **All 50 states, the District of Columbia, and Puerto Rico have safe haven laws. The exact details of the laws vary by location.** Have students research more about the laws in their state. OL

Critical Thinking

Have students discuss why they think most states require a teen father to provide financial support to a child. OL

Reading Strategy

Emphasize At this time, you may want to review the many benefits of abstinence discussed in previous lessons. OL

Home and Community

Education and Income Have students research the median salaries of people with different levels of education. Ask them to compare the average salary of a person who has not completed high school to one who has a college degree. Have students use these figures to explain why teen parents are less likely to be able to provide financially for a child. AL

ASSESS

Reteaching Have students write a short paragraph describing the qualities necessary to be a nurturing and committed parent.

Enrichment Have students observe a day-care center or assist a family with small children for several hours. Ask students to write an essay about the difficulties involved in caring for children.

Sum up the lesson by telling students that becoming a parent is a great responsibility that requires both physical and emotional maturity. Remind students that teen parents will experience many difficulties.

MODULE 4
Assessment Answers

1. To enter a lasting relationship with the person they love.

2. They understand their needs and know how to meet them in healthy ways.

3. Students' answers should include any four of the following factors: agreeing on important issues in their marriage; sharing common interests and values; demonstrating affection and sharing confidences; showing a willingness to compromise and put others first; sharing similarities in family backgrounds; having parents who had a successful marriage; not having major conflicts with their in-laws; having several good friends of both genders; having had a long period of close association prior to marriage; having stable jobs and career goals; agreeing on how they feel about raising children.

4. Parenting is providing care, support, and love in a way that leads to a child's total development. The most basic function is taking care of physical needs, such as food, clothing, shelter, and medical care.

5. She has a greater risk for complications in pregnancy, including miscarriage, and her body is not fully developed and is often not prepared for the stresses of pregnancy.

6. Students may list dropping out of school, not being able to get a good job, finding ways to spend time with his child, and being financially responsible for a child.

7. Practicing abstinence from sexual activity.

8. Answers will vary, but may include level of maturity, ability to make healthy decisions, relationship with family members, educational and career goals, and personal choices about becoming a parent someday.

9. Answers will vary, but students might discuss differences of opinion about important issues concerning their relationship, such as different interests, different backgrounds, different religions; arguments about finances; and disagreements about whether to have children and how to raise them.

10. Answers will vary. Students should point out attributes of the healthy marriage and attributes of the unhealthy marriage.

11. Answers will vary.

12. Answers will vary. Student responses should provide specific examples for comparing and contrasting and discuss the difficulties of raising a baby as a single teen.

13. Pamphlets will vary.

14. Stories will vary.

Reviewing Facts and Vocabulary

1. What is the most common reason for people to marry?

2. Describe people who have emotional and social maturity.

3. Identify four factors that can affect marital success.

4. What is *parenting*? Describe the most basic needs a parent provides for a child.

5. How can a female teen's physical health be affected by pregnancy?

6. Name two adjustments a teen male may have to make if he becomes a parent.

7. What is the only sure way to prevent pregnancy until a person is ready to become a parent?

Writing Critically

8. Analyze. Write a one-page summary describing what factors should be considered when making the decision to get married.

9. Synthesize. Consider the factors that make up a successful marriage, and write down a list of reasons why marriages may end in divorce.

10. Compare and Contrast. Make a comparison between a healthy marriage and an unhealthy marriage that you see in the media. Write a list describing what characteristics make up each kind of marriage.

11. Apply. Write a brief essay describing what goals you have set for yourself that you would have to delay or give up if you became a teen parent.

12. Compare and Contrast. Compare and contrast what it would be like to have a baby as a single teen with what it would be like to have a baby after one is emotionally mature, married, and established in a career. Provide specific examples.

Applying Health Skills

13. Advocacy. Create a pamphlet that presents teens with the benefits of remaining abstinent and avoiding teen pregnancy. You can include reasons why being a teen parent is difficult, as well as the actual demands of having and caring for a baby.

14. Communication Skills. Write a short story about a teen whose best friend wants to get married and have a baby before finishing high school. The teen should use effective communication skills to discuss with the friend the many risks of teen marriage and pregnancy. Include "I" statements, a respectful and caring tone, and good listening skills.

BEYOND THE CLASSROOM ACTIVITIES

PARENT INVOLVEMENT

Research Marriage Customs. Using the Internet or library resources, find out about marriage customs in the United States. How are they different from the customs of other countries? How are they alike? Discuss these customs with your parents and other family members.

SCHOOL AND COMMUNITY

Evaluate Community Resources. Research the amount of money it costs in your community to provide childcare for a baby or toddler during a normal 40-hour work week. Find out whether the childcare centers provide care for sick children as well. Report your findings to the class.

BEYOND THE CLASSROOM

Parent Involvement: Research Marriage Customs. Have students use the Internet or library resources to find out about marriage customs in the United States. How are they different from the customs of other countries? How are they alike? Ask students to discuss these customs with their parents and other family members.

School and Community: Evaluate Community Resources. Have students research the amount of money it costs in their community to provide childcare for a baby or toddler during a normal 40-hour work week. Have them find out whether local childcare centers provide care for sick children as well. Students should report their findings to the class.

- Encourage students to participate in activities that involve parents and the community.
- Answers will vary.

MODULE 5 | Pregnancy and Childbirth

MODULE 5	STANDARDS / NOTES	LESSON ASSESSMENT
		Module 5 Assessment Online assessment
LESSON 1 **Prenatal Development** **BIG IDEA.** A baby grows and develops through multiple stages inside the mother during pregnancy.		Lesson 1 Review Online assessment
LESSON 2 **Prenatal Care** **BIG IDEA.** During pregnancy, special care needs to be taken to ensure the fetus and mother remain healthy.		Lesson 2 Review Online assessment
LESSON 3 **Childbirth** **BIG IDEA.** A mother has many healthy options to use during the experience of labor and delivery.		Lesson 3 Review Online assessment

(30 MIN. for each lesson)

Key to Abilities   Teaching Strategies and Activities have been coded for ability level and appropriateness.

AL Activities for students working above grade level

BL Activities for students working below grade level

OL Activities for students working on grade level

EL Activities for English Learners

MODULE 5

Pregnancy and Childbirth

LESSONS

1 Prenatal Development

2 Prenatal Care

3 Childbirth

55

Pregnancy and Childbirth

Module Overview: Module 5 focus on the stages of pregnancy from conception through delivery and explores the best practices for maintaining the health of the child and mother.

LESSON 1
Identify the stages of fetal development after fertilization and examine the significance of genes and heredity.

LESSON 2
Examine the importance of prenatal care and proper nutrition for the health of a baby and the mother.

LESSON 3
Identify and explore the stages of labor and identify childbirth options and trends.

Activating Prior Knowledge

Using Visuals A newborn baby's health is greatly affected by the care taken by the mother during pregnancy.

Ask Students: *What steps can a pregnant female take to ensure that both she and her baby are as healthy as possible?*

Prenatal Development

FOCUS

BIG IDEA A baby grows and develops through multiple stages inside the mother during pregnancy.

Inform students that signs of pregnancy may include all of the following:

- A missed menstrual period.
- Nausea. Commonly known as "morning sickness," these bouts of nausea can occur throughout the day. Two-thirds of all pregnant females may experience this.
- Enlarged or tender breasts. By the eighth week of pregnancy, in many females, the areolas—the pigmented areas around the nipples—will have grown darker and larger than normal.

Reading Strategy

Predict Students' questions should include topics from all of the headings and subheadings found in the lesson. Students' questions will vary.

QUICKWRITE

Before students respond, write the following on the board for students to answer: *Name as many signs as you can that might indicate a female is pregnant.* **Accept reasonable responses.**

Student Objectives

- Explain fetal development from conception through pregnancy.
- Explain the significance of genetics and its role in fetal development.
- Discuss the importance of healthful living before and during pregnancy.

TEACH

Discussing

Have students discuss the myths people tell children about how babies are born. Ask them why they think people have told such stories. OL

Reading Strategy

Building Vocabulary As students read the lesson, have them make a chart listing the terms used to describe a child, as it develops from conception until birth, the time period each term includes, and the different characteristics of the developing child in each stage. OL

Prenatal Development

BEFORE YOU READ

Predict. Scan the headings, subheadings, and photo captions. Write a list of questions related to prenatal development. After reading the lesson, write down the answers to your questions.

Vocabulary

fertilization
zygote
blastocyst
embryo
amniotic sac
placenta
umbilical cord
fetus
genes
genetic counseling

BIG IDEA A baby grows and develops through multiple stages inside the mother during pregnancy.

QUICK WRITE

Why is it important to learn about fetal development? *Write down your ideas in a brief paragraph.*

Fertilization and Implantation

Pregnancy begins with conception, or **fertilization**. Fertilization is the union of a single sperm and an ovum. During sexual intercourse, the erect penis ejaculates hundreds of millions of sperm into the vagina. The sperm swim from the vagina through the cervix, into the uterus, and up the fallopian tubes. If an ovum is present in a fallopian tube, the first sperm that reaches the ovum can penetrate it. A fertilized ovum is called a **zygote**. After the zygote forms, it begins dividing, first into two cells, then four, then eight, and so on as it travels down the fallopian tube to the uterus—a journey that takes three to four days.

In the uterus, the zygote becomes a ball of cells with a cavity in the center, called a **blastocyst**. The blastocyst receives nourishment from secretions made by the uterine lining, or endometrium, for another few days before it begins to burrow into, or implant, in the uterine lining.

Embryonic Development

Six or seven days after fertilization, the blastocyst attaches itself to and becomes embedded in the uterine lining, which has been thickening to receive the blastocyst. This process takes a few days. From the time of implantation until about the eighth week of development, an implanted blastocyst is called an **embryo**.

The embryo grows rapidly during the next five weeks. By the sixth week, it is approximately 4/100 of an inch in size. The cells of the embryo begin to differentiate into three layers that will form the baby's organs and body systems. One layer becomes the respiratory and digestive systems; another develops into muscles, bones, blood vessels, and skin; and a third layer becomes the nervous system, sense organs, and mouth.

One of the first organs to develop is the brain. Neurons begin to develop about 18 days after fertilization. The central nervous system grows rapidly, and the head takes shape about three weeks later.

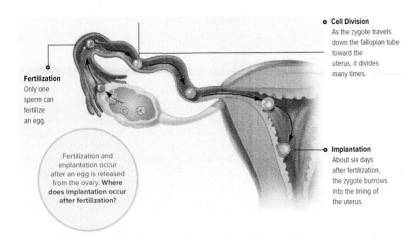

Cell Division
As the zygote travels down the fallopian tube toward the uterus, it divides many times.

Fertilization
Only one sperm can fertilize an egg.

Fertilization and implantation occur after an egg is released from the ovary. **Where does implantation occur after fertilization?**

Implantation
About six days after fertilization, the zygote burrows into the lining of the uterus.

As development continues, special membranes form around the embryo. One of these membranes becomes the **amniotic sac**. This is a fluid-filled sac that surrounds the embryo. The amniotic sac protects the embryo from outside impact and insulates it from temperature changes. The **placenta** is a structure that forms along the lining of the uterus as the embryo implants. The blood-rich tissues of the placenta transfer oxygen and nutrients from the mother's blood to the embryo's blood through the **umbilical cord**. The umbilical cord is a ropelike structure that connects the embryo and the mother's placenta. It grows to be about 20 inches long. Waste products leave the embryo's bloodstream through the umbilical cord and are then excreted from the mother's body along with her own wastes.

There is no direct exchange of blood between the mother and the embryo. Materials diffuse from one blood supply to the other through the umbilical cord.

Prenatal Development

Reading Strategy

Emphasize At this time, you may want to review the reasons why people decide to have children from a previous lesson. BL OL

Critical Thinking

Discussing Ask students why it is necessary for the fertilized ovum to travel to the uterus. **The uterus nourishes the fertilized ovum.** Ask students why they think it is important that waste products be removed from the embryo's blood and excreted through the mother's body. **So they do not build up and harm the mother or child.** OL

Reading Strategy

Emphasize Stress to students that the structures that bring the embryo nutrients also bring in any alcohol, nicotine, or other drug the mother has used. OL

Active Learning

Class Activity Ask students to list structures that help nourish and protect the developing fetus. Have them look in a biology textbook to view these structures. AL

Caption Answer: *The zygote implants itself in the lining of the uterus.*

LESSON 1
Prenatal Development

Critical Thinking

Due Date Tell students that doctors calculate the day of conception as about two weeks after the first day of the last menstrual cycle. Ask students why it is important to calculate this date. OL

Active Learning

Research Ask students to research how home pregnancy tests work. Have volunteers report to the class on the reliability of these tests. AL

Caption Answer: *human chorionic gonadotropin (HCG)*

A physician should always confirm the results of a home pregnancy test. **What hormone is detected by pregnancy tests?**

Fetal Development

By the end of the eighth week after fertilization, the major external features of the embryo are formed and the main organ systems are developing. At this point the **fetus** is only about 1¼ inches long, but is recognizable as a human being. For the remaining 30 weeks of pregnancy, the fetus will continue to grow and develop.

Determining a Pregnancy

When fertilization occurs and the blastocyst stage is reached, a hormone called human chorionic gonadotropin (HCG) is released into the mother's bloodstream. This hormone stimulates the release of two other hormones, estrogen and progesterone, which maintain the uterine lining and suppress ovulation. Some HCG passes into the urine. A simple urine test can detect the presence and amount of HCG as early as one day after a missed menstrual period. This confirms whether a female is pregnant. The urine test can be performed at a doctor's office or in the home, using a store-bought pregnancy test.

STAGES OF EMBRYONIC AND FETAL DEVELOPMENT

The time from conception to birth is usually about nine full months, which are divided into three 3-month periods called trimesters. This figure describes the changes that take place during each trimester; the images show the development of the fetus in each trimester.

	End of First Month	End of Second Month	End of Third Month
	• Measures 3/16 of an inch long • Backbone formed • Arm and leg buds begin to form • Heart forms and starts beating	• Measures 1 1/4 inches long • Weighs 1/30 of an ounce • Arms and legs distinguishable, fingers and toes well formed • Eyes visible, eyelids fused • Major blood vessels form • Internal organs continue developing	• Measures 3 inches long • Weighs 1 ounce • Eyes, nose, and ears continue to develop • Heartbeat detectable • Limbs fully formed, nails appear • Urine starts to form
	End of Fourth Month	End of Fifth Month	End of Sixth Month
	• Measures 6 1/2 to 7 inches long • Weighs 4 ounces • Head proportionally large compared to body • Face more recognizable, hair forms on head • Bones hardening, joints begin to form • Body systems develop rapidly • External sex organs identifiable	• Measures 10 to 12 inches long • Weighs 1/2 to 1 pound • Lanugo (fine hair) covers body • Fetal movements felt by mother • Head more in proportion with rest of body	• Measures 11 to 14 inches long • Weighs 1 1/4 to 1 1/2 pounds • Eyelids no longer fused, eyelashes form • Skin wrinkled and pink
	End of Seventh Month	End of Eighth Month	End of Ninth Month
	• Measures 13 to 17 inches long • Weighs 2 1/2 to 3 pounds • Fetus capable of surviving outside uterus • Body proportions more like that of full-term baby • Fetus assumes upside-down position	• Measures 16 1/2 to 18 inches long • Weighs 4 1/2 to 5 pounds • Fat deposits under skin make skin less wrinkled • In males, testes descend into scrotum • Bones of head soft	• Measures 20 inches long • Weighs 7 to 7 1/2 pounds • Additional fat deposits under skin • Lanugo falls off • Nails fully grown

MedicalRF.com

Prenatal Development

Reading Strategy

Discuss Tell students that parents can receive a test to determine the gender of their baby. Ask students what other questions parents might have about their developing baby. BL OL

Prenatal Development

Reading Strategy

Emphasize Tell students that although genes determine a person's inherited traits, not all such traits are either dominant or recessive. Some traits can be expressed as hybrids— a combination of the traits inherited from the mother and from the father. For example, the hair texture of a child with a curly-haired parent and a straight-haired parent can be wavy—a combination of the two. OL

Active Learning

Class Activity Reinforce the concept of dominant and recessive genes by making a chart showing the likelihood of a child being born with blue eyes if a) the child inherits a gene for blue eyes from each parent; or b) the child inherits a gene for brown eyes from one parent and a gene for blue eyes from the other. OL

Research Ask students to research differences in the development of multiple embryos in the uterus and share their findings with the class. AL

Writing Strategy

Hereditary Diseases Ask students to research one of the hereditary diseases discussed in the text or another hereditary disease and write one paragraph on their findings. Have students share their results with the class. AL

A radioimmunoassay is another type of pregnancy test that a doctor can perform. This test can detect HCG in urine or blood as early as a week before the expected menstrual period. A doctor will also perform an internal examination to confirm a pregnancy. Changes in the cervix and in the size of the uterus will be detected when a female is pregnant.

Home pregnancy tests became available in the 1970s. Today, they are the most common form of pregnancy testing. The test is similar to the one given in a doctor's office. However, research has shown that home pregnancy tests yield a high number of false negative results, which means that the test indicates a female is not pregnant when she really is. The unreliability of the test is mostly due to user error; thus, a female should see a physician to confirm the test results.

What Will it Be?

The sperm determines a child's gender. The sperm and the ovum each contribute one set of 23 chromosomes during fertilization. A human being, therefore, has 23 pairs of chromosomes, for a total of 46. One pair consists of specialized sex chromosomes, of which there are two types, X and Y. Ova always carry an X (female) chromosome; sperm can carry either an X or a Y. If a sperm carrying an X chromosome fertilizes an ovum, the combination is XX, and the child is female. If the sperm is carrying a Y chromosome, the combination is XY, and the child is male.

Genes and Heredity

The 23 pairs of chromosomes in the human body are made up of **genes.** Genes are units of heredity that determine which traits, or characteristics, offspring inherit from their parents. The genes we inherit determine traits such as height, hair color, and skin type. For some traits, there are two types of genes: dominant and recessive. When both are present in an individual, the dominant gene will mask the effect of the recessive gene. For example, the gene for brown eyes is dominant and the gene for blue eyes is recessive. If a child inherits a gene for blue eyes from each parent, the child will have blue eyes; if a gene for brown eyes comes from each parent, the child's eyes will be brown. However, if a child inherits a gene for brown eyes from one parent and a gene for blue eyes from the other parent, the dominant gene for brown eyes will mask the effect of the recessive gene for blue eyes, and the child will have brown eyes.

Hereditary Diseases

Certain diseases can be passed from parent to offspring through genes. The genes for some hereditary diseases are dominant; thus, only one parent has to contribute that gene for the child to have the disease. For example, the gene for Huntington's disease, which causes the progressive loss of mental functions, is dominant.

If a parent has this disease, there is a fifty percent chance that he or she will pass the disease on to the child. In hereditary diseases for which the gene is recessive, both parents must contribute the gene for their child to have the disease. Parents can carry a recessive gene for the disease without having the disease themselves if they have a dominant gene to mask it. For example, cystic fibrosis is a recessive gene disorder. In this disease, the body produces abnormally thick and sticky mucus in the lungs and other parts of the respiratory system.

Certain recessive gene diseases are carried only on the X chromosome. Because a female has two X chromosomes, she can have one dominant and one recessive gene and not have the disease. Because males have only one X chromosome, if they inherit a recessive gene for the disease, there is no paired dominant gene to mask it. Hemophilia and red-green color blindness are examples of this type of genetic disease.

Genetic Counseling

Genetics is the study of heredity. **Genetic counseling** is a process in which genetic histories of prospective parents are studied to determine the presence of certain hereditary diseases. It lets doctors map people's family histories and run medical tests to identify genetic or biochemical markers for certain hereditary diseases, such as Huntington's disease. Since most people don't show symptoms of this disease until later in life, genetic testing before pregnancy can help married couples make an informed decision about having children.

Lesson 1 Review

Facts and Vocabulary

1. List and briefly explain the major steps of fetal development from conception to birth.

2. Describe the function of the amniotic sac.

3. What does a doctor do to determine whether a female is pregnant?

4. Does the father's sperm or the mother's ovum determine a child's gender? How?

5. What are genes? List some characteristics that are inherited.

Thinking Critically

6. **Synthesize.** If a child has one parent with brown eyes and one parent with blue eyes, what color eyes will the child have? Why?

7. **Analyze.** In a short paragraph, briefly explain the significance of genetics and its role in fetal development.

Applying Health Skills

8. **Communication Skills.** Suppose a friend tells you she is not pregnant because she took a home pregnancy test and the results were negative. What would you tell her?

Prenatal Development **61**

Lesson 1 Review Answers

1. Students' answers should include multiple facts from the Stage of Embryonic and Fetal Development table in the lesson.

2. A fluid-filled sac that surrounds the embryo, protecting it from outside impact and temperature changes.

3. The doctor will administer a test and then will perform an internal examination to detect changes in the cervix and the size of the uterus that signify pregnancy.

4. The father's sperm, by carrying either an X or Y chromosome.

5. Genes are units of heredity that determine which traits offspring inherit from their parents. Inherited genes determine traits such as height, hair color, and skin type.

6. The dominant brown gene masks the effect of the recessive blue gene, so the child's eyes are brown.

7. Possible answer: Genetic counseling helps prospective parents know more about their risk of passing on genetic diseases.

8. Research has shown that home pregnancy tests yield a high number of false negative results. For that reason, if someone thinks she may be pregnant she should have a pregnancy test done by a health care professional.

Critical Thinking

Genetic Counseling Tell students that genetic counselors study a variety of topics in science, health, and counseling. Ask students to list some of the topics a genetic counselor might study. Ask students why prospective parents might consult a genetic counselor. OL

ASSESS

Reteaching Have students prepare a timeline that summarizes physical development of the fetus in the uterus throughout pregnancy.

Enrichment Have students research the history of genetic counseling. Have them report on their findings to the class. Sum up the lesson by discussing with students fertilization and fetal development from conception through birth.

Prenatal Care

FOCUS

BIG IDEA During pregnancy, special care needs to be taken to ensure the fetus and mother remain healthy. Point out to students that it is important that the mother take care of the developing fetus to help ensure that the baby will be born healthy.

Reading Strategy

Explain Students' answers will vary, but should include improving nutrition, avoiding alcohol, tobacco, and other drugs, and receiving regular medical care.

> ### QUICKWRITE
>
> Before students answer, write the following on the board for students to answer: *Why is it important for a female to learn about proper prenatal care as soon as she thinks she might be pregnant?* **Accept reasonable responses.**

Student Objectives

- Analyze how alcohol, tobacco, and other drugs affect the fetus.
- Explain the importance of the role of prenatal care and proper nutrition for the baby and mother.
- Examine how technology has impacted families by aiding in prenatal diagnosis of certain conditions.

TEACH

Reading Strategy

Building Vocabulary In the last lesson, students learned that the protective sac surrounding the embryo is called the amniotic sac. Inform students that *centesis* comes from the Greek, meaning "to puncture." Have students write their own definition of the word *amniocentesis*. Have them check their definition in the Glossary/Glossario. OL

Prenatal Care

BIG IDEA During pregnancy, special care needs to be taken to ensure the fetus and mother remain healthy.

BEFORE YOU READ

Explain. Write a summary describing what the term *prenatal care* means. What behaviors might a mother change to take care of her baby before it is born?

Vocabulary
prenatal
obstetrician
fetal alcohol syndrome (FAS)
rubella
ultrasound
amniocentesis
chorionic villi sampling (CVS)
birth defect

> **QUICK WRITE**
>
> List three things a pregnant female should do and three things she should not do to ensure the health of her baby.

Characteristics of a Pregnancy

Early signs of pregnancy vary. Some signs such as food cravings, headaches, swollen/tender breasts, and spotting or cramping may be mistaken for the start of a menstrual period. That's why early testing is important. The sooner a female confirms her pregnancy, the sooner the **prenatal** care can begin. Prenatal means occurring or existing before birth. Prenatal care increases the odds of a healthy pregnancy.

A normal pregnancy lasts about nine full months. Pregnancy can be divided into three trimesters, or periods of three months, each characterized by physical changes and symptoms:

- **First trimester.** The breasts become fuller and tender, and blood vessels in the breasts become more prominent. The areola, the area around each nipple, darkens. Many females experience morning sickness—nausea or vomiting that occurs most frequently in the morning—and even mild exertion can bring on fatigue.

- **Second trimester.** The fetus continues to grow, causing the abdomen to swell; the mother can detect fetal movements. Both appetite and blood volume increase. Morning sickness usually subsides, and many females report feeling healthy and energetic during this time.

- **Third trimester.** Pregnancy is almost always visible by the third trimester. Most females will have gained 25 to 35 pounds by the time of delivery. Blood volume has increased by 30 to 40 percent, the mother's heart beats faster, and the uterus is stretched to many times its original size. After the birth, the uterus contracts to nearly its pre-pregnancy size. The growing fetus takes up enough room to crowd the mother's bladder, stomach, and lungs.

Mental/Emotional Changes

Hormonal changes cause many pregnant females to become more emotional or experience mood swings similar to those associated with premenstrual syndrome (PMS). In the first trimester, feelings can range from joy to fear to excitement. In the second trimester, hormonal shifts may cause forgetfulness. Some females may also have difficulty concentrating. As a pregnant female gains weight, her center of gravity changes and her ligaments loosen; this may cause her to feel more clumsy than usual. In the third trimester, worries about labor, delivery, and the health of the baby are all normal. Talking about these feelings with a partner, a physician, or another pregnant female can be helpful.

During the second trimester, most pregnant females feel healthy and energetic. **How long does a normal pregnancy last?**

Common Discomforts

The growing fetus causes changes in a female's body that can bring on a range of discomforts during pregnancy. The need to urinate increases, and many females experience leg cramps. Headaches, particularly in the first trimester, are also common. In the later months, back pain can result from increased weight in the front, and water retention causes swelling of the hands, ankles, and feet. Minor contractions and sleep problems may occur. Weight gain can result in the development of stretch marks, which a pregnant female may find unsightly. With the exception of stretch marks, these discomforts usually end after delivery.

Components of Prenatal Care

The care a female takes during pregnancy affects her own health, as well as that of her developing baby. Regular medical care, a well-balanced eating plan, regular exercise, and avoidance of harmful substances such as tobacco, alcohol, and other drugs are all responsible choices that a pregnant female can make.

Axel Skelley/Blend Images/Getty Images

Prenatal Care **63**

Critical Thinking

Pregnancy and Health Have students discuss how changes brought on by pregnancy might affect the physical, mental/emotional, and social health of the mother. Have students think of strategies to help a pregnant female deal with the changes she is experiencing. OL

Active Learning

Research Have students work in groups to research and learn about the services and classes your community offers expectant parents. AL

Caption Answer: *Nine months*

Prenatal Care

Critical Thinking

Prenatal Care Ask students how the role of prenatal care might be different for females with medical complications. AL

Reading Strategy

Emphasize A pregnant female should consult with her doctor about her physical activity routine to ensure that she and her developing baby will not have any problems. BL OL

Caption Answer: *Protein, calcium, and vitamin E.*

Medical Care

The main component of prenatal care is a schedule of regular visits with an **obstetrician** or certified nurse-midwife. An obstetrician is a doctor who specializes in the area of pregnant females and their developing fetuses, and who are present at the birth of the baby. Both types of health care providers are trained in prenatal care and delivery of babies. The obstetrician or nurse-midwife takes a medical history and gives the pregnant female a complete physical examination. This includes blood and urine tests as well as a pelvic examination. Regular visits are usually scheduled once a month through the seventh month, every two weeks in the eighth month, and weekly in the ninth month. At each visit, the mother's weight and blood pressure will be taken, her urine tested, her abdomen measured, and from week 12 onward the fetal heartbeat will be monitored.

Nutrition

A pregnant female needs to consume more nutrients to ensure the health of the developing fetus. She needs:

- extra protein for her own strength and for the development of the placenta, amniotic sac, and fetal brain.
- extra calcium to build strong fetal bones and teeth.
- vitamin E for tissue growth and red blood cells.
- iron for red blood cells to fight against fatigue and possibly anemia.
- prenatal vitamins to provide adequate nutrients.
- folic acid, which is a critical part of spinal fluid and helps close the tube that contains the central nervous system. This neural tube forms 17 to 30 days after conception, so neural tube defects can occur before a female knows that she is pregnant. Health care professionals suggest that all females of childbearing age consume 400 to 600 micrograms of folic acid daily to prevent neural tube defects. However, the March of Dimes recommends women limit folic acid consumption to no more than 1,000 micrograms a day.

For females who are at a healthy pre-pregnancy weight, gaining more than 35 pounds during pregnancy can be a health risk for both mother and baby. Daily caloric intake should increase by only about 300 calories, and those additional calories should come from nutritious foods, including those rich in calcium and protein.

Exercise

Regular exercise is important during pregnancy. In a normal pregnancy, a healthy female can continue most activities she participated in before she became pregnant . Walking and swimming are particularly good activities during pregnancy.

Good nutrition ensures that a pregnant female receives the nutrients required for proper fetal development. **What are three important nutrients pregnant females need to consume?**

Vladimir Pcholkin/Getty Images

Medical Complications

In a normal pregnancy, there are no major problems. Proper prenatal care can help identify and treat medical complications when they do arise.

- **Rh Factor in Blood.** Rh factor is a protein on the surface of red blood cells. About 85 percent of people have this antigen in their blood and are called Rh+ (Rh positive). Those who do not have it are Rh– (Rh negative). When an Rh– person receives Rh+ blood, their blood builds up antibodies against the Rh antigen. If an Rh– mother and an Rh+ father have an Rh+ baby, the mother's antibodies can cross the placenta and attack the baby's red blood cells. Treatment of the mother with a serum known as Rh immune globulin can prevent the buildup of antibodies, but the problem must be diagnosed early to avoid serious fetal complications.

- **Pregnancy-Induced Hypertension and Preeclampsia** The mother's blood pressure normally rises a bit around the seventh month, but about 5 percent of pregnant females develop prolonged high blood pressure, or pregnancy-induced hypertension (PIH).

If PIH is accompanied by sudden weight gain, severe swelling from water retention, and/or protein in the urine, the female has a condition known as preeclampsia. If untreated, this condition can lead to many health problems for the mother, ranging from blurred vision and headaches to convulsions and coma. Preeclampsia can also cause stunted growth and developmental disabilities in the fetus. First-time mothers in their early teens or those over age 35 are most at risk. Complete bed rest and medication can increase the chances of a full-term delivery, but sometimes the baby must be delivered early to protect both mother and baby.

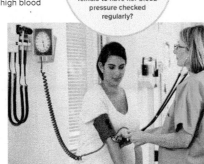

Regular prenatal checkups can help identify potential complications during pregnancy. **Why is it important for a pregnant female to have her blood pressure checked regularly?**

Dangers to the Fetus

Although mother and baby do not directly share any blood, substances in the mother's bloodstream cross the placenta and enter the fetus's blood. No medication should be taken without a physician's advice, and alcohol, tobacco, and illegal drugs should be avoided entirely.

Tobacco

Tobacco use is harmful to both mother and baby. Babies born to females who smoke can have lower birth weights, heart and brain abnormalities, and cleft lips and palates. Smoking has been linked to higher fetal and infant mortality rates, as well as sudden infant death syndrome (SIDS), a condition in which a seemingly healthy baby dies for no apparent reason. According to the American Lung Association, pregnant females exposed repeatedly to secondhand smoke have an increased risk of having a low-birth-weight baby.

Writing Strategy

Research Have students conduct research on the health risks and problems associated with low birth weight. Have students write a paragraph explaining their findings. Let volunteers share their findings with the class. AL

Caption Answer: *The female may have a condition called pregnancy-induced hypertension.*

LESSON 2
Prenatal Care

Critical Thinking

Analyzing Responsibility Divide the class into two groups. Ask them to debate the issue of responsibility regarding fetal exposure to drugs and alcohol. For example, should females be held accountable for damage to a fetus caused by drug use? Should bartenders be required by law to withhold alcoholic beverages from females who are obviously pregnant? OL

Caption Answer: *Fetal alcohol syndrome can cause a baby to be born with physical, mental, and behavioral abnormalities if the mother drinks alcohol while she is pregnant.*

Alcohol consumption during pregnancy can cause many serious health problems in the fetus. **What is fetal alcohol syndrome (FAS)?**

Alcohol.

Fetal alcohol syndrome (FAS) is a condition of physical, mental, and behavioral abnormalities that can result when a pregnant female drinks alcohol. Effects on the fetus include:

- Low birth weight
- General weakness
- Possible speech impairment
- Poor coordination
- Stunted growth
- Cleft palate
- Facial and heart defects
- Developmental disabilities
- Poor attention span
- Inability to understand the consequences of actions
- Hyperactivity

Fetal alcohol syndrome cannot occur unless alcohol is consumed. The safest decision for pregnant females and those considering pregnancy is not to drink any alcoholic beverages.

Medication and Drugs

All medications and supplements must be approved for use during pregnancy by a health care professional. This includes prescription and over-the-counter products, as well as those labeled "natural" or "herbal." Many seemingly safe substances can harm the fetus.

All illegal drugs are unsafe and can cause serious health problems in the fetus. These include mental disabilities, respiratory problems, visual and hearing disabilities, learning and emotional problems, low birth weight, and even death. A baby can also be born addicted to a drug and have to go through the painful and dangerous process of withdrawal.

Caffeine. Some studies suggest that consuming caffeinated products during pregnancy may pose health risks to the fetus. Some caffeinated products include coffee, tea, chocolate, and colas. Many females choose to avoid caffeine during pregnancy to help ensure their baby's health.

Rubella

Rubella (German measles) is a contagious disease caused by a virus that does not cause serious complications except in pregnancy. Most pregnant females are immune to rubella either through vaccination or because they had the disease as children. Nevertheless, up to 20 percent of females of childbearing age are not immune to the disease.

- Symptoms include a rash, swollen glands, and joint pain, particularly in adults.
- If a pregnant female contracts rubella, especially during the first trimester, her fetus may develop severe birth defects. These include vision and hearing loss, heart defects, and developmental disabilities.

McGraw-Hill Education

- Rubella infection can cause miscarriage, which is the spontaneous expulsion of a fetus before the twentieth week of pregnancy. It may also cause still birth, the expulsion of a dead fetus from the body after the twentieth week of pregnancy.
- If a female contracts rubella after 20 weeks of pregnancy, birth defects are rare.

Radiation

Direct exposure to radiation can harm a developing fetus, so it is best to avoid routine X-rays such as those taken by a dentist. If X-rays are necessary, however, as in the case of a broken bone, a protective apron can be placed over the abdomen to shield it from radiation.

Lead

Maternal exposure to lead can also endanger a fetus. When lead in the mother's bloodstream passes through the placenta to the fetus's blood, it can cause developmental defects and mental deficiency. One common source of lead is paint in buildings built before 1978, when lead-based paint was banned. Maternal lead exposure can also cause higher rates of miscarriage, premature birth, and stillbirth.

Sexually Transmitted Diseases

Sexually transmitted infections (STIs), otherwise known as sexually transmitted diseases (STDs), are diseases spread through sexual contact; some are very harmful to a fetus and newborn. Because of the serious threat posed by STDs, pregnant females are tested for these diseases at the first prenatal visit with their health care professional. Some STDs can be cured, but others can be only treated. Females who know they have an STD should seek treatment before they become pregnant.

EFFECTS OF STDS ON THE FETUS AND INFANT

STD	Time of Transmission	Harm to Fetus/Infant	Treatment
Chlamydia	During delivery	Premature delivery, eye and respiratory infections, blindness, pneumonia	Antibiotics
Gonorrhea	During delivery	Blindness, joint infections, blood infections	Antibiotics
Herpes	During delivery	Fatal infections, lesions on eyes or mouth	No cure; antiviral medications can minimize outbreaks; cesarean delivery can protect the baby
Human papillomavirus (HPV)	During delivery	Development of warts in throat or voice box	No cure; surgery to prevent warts from blocking throat
Syphilis	During pregnancy	Stillbirth, developmental delays, seizures, death shortly after birth	Intramuscular injection of antibiotic
HIV	During pregnancy/delivery/ breastfeeding	Weak immune system, thrush, bacterial infections, neurological problems, enlarged lymph nodes, liver, and spleen	No cure; AZT helps prevent transmission from mother to child

Prenatal Care

Active Learning

Class Activity Ask students to examine the chart on "The Effects of STDs on the Fetus and Infant." Have students work in small groups. Assign each group one of the STDs in the chart. Have them research more about the symptoms, treatment, and effects of the STD on infected persons. Allow time for groups to present their information to the class. AL

LESSON 2
Prenatal Care

Reading Strategy

Explain The living cells in the amniotic fluid removed during amniocentesis are cultured, or grown in a laboratory. During the subsequent analysis of the chromosomes for abnormalities, the chromosomes are paired and identified. The pairing of sex chromosomes indicates the sex of the fetus: XX for a female, XY for a male. Ask students to discuss the reasons why parents might or might not want to know the sex of their baby before it is born. OL

Prenatal Testing Ask students how prenatal testing might help the survival of a baby born with a genetic birth defect. AL

Active Learning

Research Have students work in small groups to choose a birth defect and research its causes and treatments, if any. Have groups compile their findings and create an informative booklet on birth defects. AL

Caption Answer: *Ultrasound can be used throughout pregnancy to assess fetal position and development.*

Tests During Pregnancy

Prenatal tests may be ordered to see if a fetus is at risk for various health problems. Sometimes a problem can be treated before the baby is born.

Ultrasound

The fetus can be seen in the uterus by using **ultrasound**. This is a test that produces an image on a screen by reflecting sound waves off the body's inner structures. The embryo is visible by four weeks after fertilization, and the fetal heartbeat can be identified at five weeks. To produce an image, an instrument called a transducer is moved across the abdomen; a computer translates the reflections into images on a monitor. Ultrasound can be used throughout pregnancy to assess fetal position and development.

Amniocentesis

Amniocentesis is a procedure that reveals chromosomal abnormalities and certain metabolic disorders in the fetus. First, ultrasound is used to determine the position of the fetus. Then the doctor inserts a long needle through the abdomen and into the amniotic sac and removes one to two tablespoons of amniotic fluid. The fluid contains living cells from the fetus that are tested for chromosomal abnormalities. They also reveal the gender and age of the fetus. Amniocentesis is usually performed 16 to 20 weeks after fertilization. The procedure carries a small risk of miscarriage. Because of this risk, amniocentesis is usually recommended only for those females who have an increased risk of having a child with chromosomal or genetic abnormalities. Factors that may contribute to these abnormalities include the following:

- The mother is 35 years of age or older.
- The mother has had a previous child or fetus with a birth defect.
- There is a family history of certain chromosomal or genetic disorders.

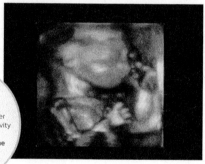

An ultrasound allows a fetus to be observed without exposing either the mother or the fetus to the radioactivity of X-rays. **During a pregnancy, what are some things an ultrasound can be used for?**

Chorionic Villi Sampling

In addition to amniocentesis, a test used to reveal genetic disorders and fetal age and gender is **chorionic villi sampling (CVS)**. In this procedure, a thin tube is inserted through the vagina and the cervix. A small sample of chorionic villi tissue, which is attached to the sac that contains the fetus, is removed. The test is usually done between 10 and 12 weeks after a female's last menstrual period; results are available within 10 days. CVS is slightly more likely than amniocentesis to cause miscarriage. Like amniocentesis, CVS is usually offered only to pregnant females who have an increased risk of giving birth to a child with genetic or chromosomal abnormalities. Some parents choose CVS because the test can be performed earlier than amniocentesis.

Birth Defects

A **birth defect** is an irregularity in the structure or function of the body that is present at birth. Birth defects can be caused by irregular genes or by environmental factors. According to the March of Dimes, approximately 150,000 infants are born with birth defects each year in the United States. There are more than 4,000 known birth defects.

Environmental factors that may cause birth defects include maternal exposure to toxins, maternal diseases, and maternal substance abuse. They also include problems that may arise during delivery, such as when the fetus does not receive an adequate supply of oxygen. Many physical disorders, such as cleft lip and clubfoot, are visible at birth. Mental disabilities, such as cerebral palsy and brain dysfunction, may not be observed until the child is older. Other conditions that are present at birth may not be apparent until the child is several months to a year old, or even older. Sickle-cell anemia and cystic fibrosis are examples of such disorders.

Character Check

Pregnant females have a responsibility to protect the developing fetus by avoiding the use of harmful substances such as tobacco, alcohol, and other drugs. Create a video explaining why it is especially important for a female to avoid using harmful substances during pregnancy.

Lesson 2 Review

Facts and Vocabulary

1. List two physical changes that occur during each trimester.

2. How can alcohol, tobacco, other drugs, and environmental hazards harm a fetus?

3. What is fetal alcohol syndrome?

4. Name two tests that can be done during pregnancy to see if the baby is at risk for a genetic or chromosomal abnormality.

Thinking Critically

5. **Synthesize.** Explain the importance of the role of prenatal care and proper nutrition in promoting optimal health for both the baby and the mother.

6. **Analyze.** Briefly explain how technology has impacted the health status of families by aiding in prenatal diagnosis of certain conditions.

Applying Health Skills

7. **Refusal Skills.** Suppose you have an older sister who is pregnant. Some of her friends are trying to convince her that it's okay to drink alcohol during her pregnancy. Explain to her why she needs to use refusal skills, and suggest ways to say no effectively.

Prenatal Care **69**

Lesson 2 Review Answers

1. Possible answers: weight gain, nausea, discomfort, hormonal changes.

2. Harmful substances cause low birth weight, fetal alcohol syndrome, and other complications.

3. It is a condition of physical, mental, and behavioral abnormalities that can result when a pregnant female drinks alcohol.

4. Amniocentesis and chorionic villi sampling

5. Possible answer: Prenatal care can help a pregnant female make healthy choices about diet, exercise, and avoiding harmful substances.

6. Development of medical technologies including ultrasound, amniocentesis, and chorionic villi sampling helps doctors and parents monitor fetal development and respond to abnormalities or complications.

7. Answers will vary, but students should explain to the sister why alcohol is harmful and should offer refusal strategies.

Prenatal Care

Active Learning

Research Have students contact birth defect prevention organizations (such as the March of Dimes), or look for their websites, to learn more about programs for fighting birth defects. Have students report their findings to the class. AL

ASSESS

Reteaching Have students reread the sections "Medical Complications" and "Dangers to the Fetus". Ask them to name the factors over which they have control. Have them explain what steps can be taken to avoid problems during pregnancy.

Enrichment Have students research fetal alcohol syndrome and report their findings to the class.

Sum up the lesson by asking students to discuss the role of good prenatal care in a healthy pregnancy and child.

LESSON 3
Childbirth

FOCUS

BIG IDEA A mother has many healthy options to use during the experience of labor and delivery.

Reading Strategy

Organize Information Students' charts will vary.

QUICKWRITE

Before students answer, write the following on the board for students to answer: *Look up the definition of* cesarean *in the dictionary.* **Explain that the word** *cesarean* **came from the Roman emperor Julius Caesar, who was supposedly born by cesarean section. Have students compare the dictionary definition with that in the Glossary/Glosario.**

Student Objectives

- Identify and explain the stages of labor.
- Explain how breastfeeding promotes optimal health for the baby.
- Identify childbirth options and trends.

TEACH

Active Learning

Guest Speaker Invite a childbirth instructor from the community to describe the birth process and the different birthing methods, and to tell how the mother may cope with the pain associated with childbirth. OL

Critical Thinking

Ask students why it might be helpful for a new mother-to-be to talk about labor to a female who has had children. OL

Childbirth

BEFORE YOU READ

Organize Information. Create a chart listing the stages of labor. Under each section, describe what happens during that stage.

Vocabulary
labor
episiotomy
cesarean birth
birthing centers

BIG IDEA A mother has many healthy options to use during the experience of labor and delivery.

QUICK WRITE

Briefly explain why a pregnant female needs to have regular exams by a health care professional.

Stages of Labor

At the end of the pregnancy, the hormone oxytocin causes uterine contractions that begin to pull open the cervix. This is the beginning of the birthing process. **Labor** is the process by which contractions gradually push the baby out of the uterus and into the vagina to be born. Though each female's pregnancy and delivery is unique, it is important to understand the typical stages leading up to labor. Labor has three stages:

- **First Stage of Labor.** Contractions gradually open the cervix to a diameter of about four inches. This process of dilation is the first, and usually the longest, stage of labor. The amniotic sac is a membrane filled with fluid that cushions the baby as it develops. The pressure of the baby's head against the amniotic sac during this stage or the next usually causes the sac to rupture, or the pregnant female's water to "break." About a pint of amniotic fluid is released from the vagina. The first stage may last for 12 hours or longer.

- **Second Stage of Labor.** When the cervix is fully dilated, the mother feels an urge to push. She uses muscles to aid the contractions in pushing the baby's head through the cervix and into the vagina. When the baby's head crowns, or is visible at the vaginal opening, the mother continues pushing until the baby is delivered. This stage generally lasts from half an hour to two hours. Rather than risk tearing the tissues around the vaginal opening, a doctor will sometimes perform an **episiotomy**. This is an incision made from the vagina toward the anus to enlarge the opening for delivery of a baby. The incision is stitched back together after birth.

- The final stage of labor lasts about 20 minutes. Contractions separate the placenta from the uterine wall and expel the placenta from the uterus and out of the body through the vagina. The detached placenta is called the afterbirth.

Delivery by Cesarean

Cesarean birth is a method of childbirth in which a surgical incision is made through the abdominal wall and uterus. The baby is lifted out through the surgical incision. The incidence of cesarean birth, also called cesarean section (C-section), has risen dramatically in recent years, accounting for more than 31 percent of U.S. births. Some C-sections are performed because the baby is not positioned correctly or does not progress into the vagina. A doctor may recommend a C-section because the mother's pelvic structure makes a vaginal delivery dangerous or even impossible. C-sections are also used to avoid transmission of certain STDs to the baby as it passes through the vagina. A pregnant female should discuss her views on C-section with her health care provider before labor begins.

Medication During Labor

Some females deliver their babies without pain medication. For those who need pain relief, several medications can be used. Some females find that pain medication relaxes them and helps them deal with the contractions. Others find that the drugs make them too drowsy to concentrate and participate fully in the birth. The effect of pain medications on the baby depends on the amount administered and how close to delivery the drug is given to the mother. If, for example, medications are given shortly before birth, the baby may be drowsy or have difficulty breathing.

When total pain relief is needed, an epidural block is used. Medication is injected through a tube inserted between the vertebrae into the spine. This provides total numbness from the waist down. Epidurals are used during C-sections and some vaginal births. General anesthesia, where the female is unconscious, is used almost exclusively for high-risk cesarean births.

After Delivery

Nursing can begin as soon as the baby is born. While the mother is not yet producing milk, her breasts secrete colostrum, a low-fat, high-carbohydrate, protein-rich fluid. Colostrum is easy to digest and has a laxative effect on the newborn.

After a few days, the breasts begin to produce milk. Both colostrum and milk contain antibodies from the mother; therefore, breast-fed babies get fewer illnesses than babies who are not breast-fed. Breast milk is nutritionally ideal for almost all babies, it doesn't cost anything, it's easier to digest than formula, and it's always ready. Babies aren't allergic to breast milk, but many are allergic to formulas based on cow's milk or soy protein. For these reasons, most pediatricians recommend breast milk over formula.

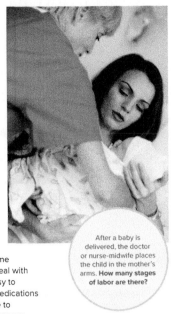

After a baby is delivered, the doctor or nurse-midwife places the child in the mother's arms. **How many stages of labor are there?**

Childbirth

Reading Strategy

Building Vocabulary Tell students that the word *labor* is used to describe many types of physical and mental work. Ask students why they think this word is also used for childbirth. BL OL EL

Writing Support

Cesarean Deliveries Have students research the increase in cesarean deliveries over the past several decades and write a brief report summarizing their findings. AL

Critical Thinking

Medication During Labor Ask students to discuss why some mothers choose not to have any pain medication when they give birth. BL

Caption Answer: *There are three stages of labor.*

LESSON 3
Childbirth

Active Learning

Delivery Methods Ask students to contact birthing centers in your community, or research their websites, to learn about the types of services they offer. Ask students to research different birthing methods and share what they find with the class. AL

Research Have students research the ways a father-to-be participates in the prenatal care and delivery of his child. AL

Critical Thinking

Discussing Ask students to list what items new parents need to help take care of their baby. Encourage them to find out about the costs of these items. OL

Caption Answer: *Cesarean birth involves a surgical incision through the mother's abdominal wall and uterus, and then the baby is lifted out.*

Birthing rooms are designed so that a female can remain in the same hospital room for labor, delivery, and recovery. **Describe the process of cesarean birth.**

Childbirth: Options and Trends

Many parents choose to educate themselves about the process of childbirth. They attend classes in birthing methods such as Lamaze or Bradley. Most doctors and nurse-midwives recommend that expectant parents attend some type childbirth classes to learn what to expect at each stage of labor and delivery. The father, a close friend, or a relative learns to play the role of coach; the mother learns relaxation and breathing techniques that enable her to cope with the pain of labor and perhaps have a medication-free delivery. The goal is to make the experience less mysterious and as painless as possible.

Many parents also take classes to learn how to perform CPR, or cardiopulmonary resuscitation, on an infant. They also learn home safety tips, such as how to keep infants safe around potential hazards. These might include electrical appliances, stairs, bathtubs, poisonous medicines, and household cleaners.

Another choice parents can make is where to have their baby. A popular option today is **birthing centers.** These are facilities that have homelike settings, are separate from a hospital, and offer medication-free births. In hospital maternity wards, nurses and doctors deliver the baby. Birthing centers, however, are staffed by certified midwives. Midwives are not registered nurses, but receive training specifically for childbirth. Birthing centers are not designed to handle emergencies and are usually available only for low-risk pregnancies. Because of this, midwives do not perform cesarean sections. However, birthing centers are often located near a hospital in case an emergency does arise. Many hospitals now have their own in-house birthing centers.

REAL WORLD CONNECTION

Health Information in the News

Recently, news organizations noted an interesting and significant trend in teen pregnancies in the United States, based on statistics from the National Center for Health Statistics. The graph below reflects some of these statistics for pregnancies among females 15 to 19 years of age from 1940 to 2011.

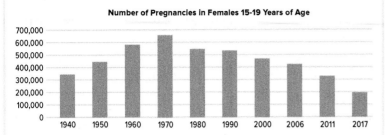

Number of Pregnancies in Females 15-19 Years of Age

Activity: Statistics

Work in groups of two or three to answer the following questions: How would you describe the overall trend(s) since 1940? In which year were pregnancies highest among this age group? Approximately what percentage decrease occurred between 1970 and 2017? If the trend continues, approximately what number would you expect to see in 2030? Discuss possible reasons for the decline of the last five decades. Be prepared to present your findings to the class.

Lesson 3 Review

Facts and Vocabulary

1. Briefly describe what occurs during each of the three stages of labor.

2. Explain what an episiotomy is and why it is used.

3. What is a cesarean birth?

4. When parents attend classes in birthing methods, what is the goal?

Thinking Critically

5. **Synthesize.** Explain how breastfeeding promotes optimal health for the baby.

6. **Analyze.** How is a childbirth preparation course helpful to an expectant mother?

Applying Health Skills

7. **Stress Management.** In addition to helping a pregnant female prepare for childbirth, classes in birthing methods also teach the expectant mother how to relax. Why might stress interfere with labor and delivery? What are some stress-management techniques a female could use throughout her pregnancy?

Childbirth **73**

LESSON 3
Childbirth

REAL WORLD CONNECTION

Health Information in the News As students examine the trends, point out the decline in teen pregnancies since 1970. Ask: *What factors may have influenced the decline in the number of pregnancies over the last 3 decades?*

ASSESS

Reteaching Have students (male and female) write a short essay on what it would be like to either experience or be with someone going through the three stages of labor.

Enrichment Have students do a study of midwifery—the use of midwives in childbirth. What is involved? How often are midwives used in the United States? What percentage of these are women? How often are midwives used in other parts of the world? What kind of training is required? In what kinds of settings do midwives usually practice? What might be the benefits and drawbacks of using a midwife during childbirth?

Sum up the lesson and module by asking students to name the many factors influencing the outcome of each birth.

Lesson 3 Review Answers

1. First stage: Contractions begin and amniotic sac usually ruptures. Second stage: Cervix is fully dilated; pushing and contractions force the baby through the cervix, into the vagina, and out through the vaginal opening. Third stage: Contractions separate the placenta from the uterine wall and expel it.

2. An episiotomy is an incision made from the vagina toward the anus to enlarge the opening for delivery of a baby and to prevent the vaginal opening from tearing.

3. A cesarean birth is a method of childbirth in which a surgical incision is made through the abdominal wall and uterus and the baby is lifted out.

4. The goal is to make the experience of labor and delivery less mysterious and as painless as possible.

5. Infants who are breastfed receive antibodies from their mother's colostrum and breast milk, so they have fewer illnesses.

6. The expectant mother will know what to expect during labor and delivery, and the female will have relaxation and breathing techniques to cope with the pain.

7. She could use stress-management techniques such as knowing how and when to relax, keeping a positive outlook, being physically active, and managing her time to deal with problems throughout her pregnancy.

LESSON 3   **73**

MODULE 5
Assessment Answers

1. The union of a single sperm and an ovum. Pregnancy begins with fertilization.

2. At the end of the third month.

3. The couples' family histories can be mapped, and medical tests can be run to identify genetic or biochemical markers for some hereditary diseases.

4. The mother's abdomen swells, she can detect fetal movements, her appetite and blood volume increase, any morning sickness usually subsides. Hormonal shifts may cause forgetfulness; some females may have trouble concentrating. Weight gain changes the female's center of gravity and loosens ligaments, causing some females to feel clumsy.

5. Babies born to smokers can have lower birth weights, heart and brain abnormalities, and cleft lip and palate. Maternal smoking is also linked to higher fetal and infant mortality rates, and SIDS.

6. To assess fetal position or evaluate development.

7. There are more than 4,000 known birth defects. They can be caused by abnormal genes or environmental factors.

8. When the cervix is fully dilated, the mother feels an urge to push. She uses muscles to aid the contractions in moving the baby's head through the cervix and into the vagina. When the baby's head crowns, the mother continues to push until the entire baby is delivered. This stage usually lasts from a half hour to 2 hours.

9. Parents learn what to expect at each stage of labor and delivery. A father, close friend, or relative learns to play the role of coach, and mothers learn relaxation and breathing techniques to cope with the pain of labor and possibly to have a medication-free delivery.

10. A birthing center is a facility that has homelike settings, is separate from a hospital, and offers medication-free births.

11. The placenta, which forms along the lining of the uterus, transfers oxygen and nutrients to the embryo, then the fetus, via the umbilical cord.

12. The doctor will likely suspect preeclampsia. Other symptoms that would confirm this diagnosis are severe swelling from water retention, and/or protein in the urine.

13. A doctor may schedule a cesarean if the baby is not positioned correctly, if the mother's pelvic structure makes a vaginal delivery dangerous or impossible, or if the mother has an STD that could be transmitted during a vaginal delivery.

14. Pamphlets will vary. Students should provide as many reasons as possible.

15. Answers will vary, but students should communicate as much information as possible about healthful behaviors during pregnancy and labor and delivery.

Reviewing Facts and Vocabulary

1. What is *fertilization*? How is it related to pregnancy?

2. When is the developing fetus's heartbeat detectable?

3. What happens during genetic counseling?

4. Describe the physical and mental/emotional changes a female may experience during her second trimester of pregnancy.

5. How can tobacco use affect a developing baby?

6. List one reason why a pregnant female would have an ultrasound.

7. About how many known birth defects are there? What can cause them?

8. Describe the second stage of labor.

9. What is taught in childbirth preparation classes?

10. What is a *birthing center*?

Writing Critically

11. Synthesize. Write a paragraph describing how the placenta and umbilical cord are integral to the nourishment of the embryo and fetus.

12. Analyze. A pregnant female experiences a sudden weight gain. She visits her doctor, who finds that her blood pressure is very high. Write a brief summary describing what condition the doctor would likely suspect. What other symptoms will the doctor check for? Explain your answers.

13. Analyze. Write a brief summary explaining why a doctor might recommend a cesarean birth instead of allowing labor and delivery to progress naturally.

Applying Health Skills

14. Advocacy. Create a pamphlet that encourages females to seek medical care when they are pregnant. List the reasons why medical care is important throughout the pregnancy as well as during labor and delivery. Make your pamphlet as attractive and informative as possible.

15. Practicing Healthful Behaviors. Review the information presented in this module. Talk with a pair of prospective parents. Discuss with them what you have learned about healthful behaviors during pregnancy and the birth process.

BEYOND THE CLASSROOM ACTIVITIES

PARENT INVOLVEMENT
Medication Options. Do research at the library or on the Internet to learn more about the pros and cons of using various medications during labor and delivery. Discuss this issue with your parents or guardians and ask what their views are on the subject.

SCHOOL AND COMMUNITY
Treatment Options. Identify ways that these symptoms can be treated. Present your findings to the class.

BEYOND THE CLASSROOM

Parent Involvement: Medication Options. Students should conduct research at the library or on the Internet to learn more about the pros and cons of using various medications during labor and delivery. Have students discuss this issue with their parents or guardians and ask what their views are on the subject.

School and Community: Treatment Options. Have students research the symptoms of postpartum depression at the school or community library and identify ways that these symptoms can be treated. Students should present their findings to the class.

- Encourage students to participate in activities that involve parents and the community.
- Answers will vary.

MODULE 6 | Issues of Sexuality

MODULE 6	STANDARDS / NOTES ✏	LESSON ASSESSMENT
	Use this space for standards and notes.	Module 6 Assessment Online assessment
LESSON 1 **Contraception** **BIG IDEA.** It is important for teens to make responsible choices about sexual behavior. *(30 MIN.)*		Lesson 1 Review Online assessment
LESSON 2 **Concerns About Sexuality** **BIG IDEA.** Understanding sexual feelings is an important part of physical, mental/emotional, and social health. *(30 MIN.)*		Lesson 2 Review Online assessment
LESSON 3 **Sexual Abuse and Violence** **BIG IDEA.** Sexual activity can have serious consequences on a teen's life. *(30 MIN.)*		Lesson 3 Review Online assessment

Key to Abilities Teaching Strategies and Activities have been coded for ability level and appropriateness.

AL Activities for students working above grade level

BL Activities for students working below grade level

OL Activities for students working on grade level

EL Activities for English Learners

MODULE 6

Issues of Sexuality

Module Overview Module 6 focuses on difficult issues of sexuality including; contraception and abstinence, sexual orientation and stereotypes, and sexual abuse and incest.

LESSON 1
Analyze the importance of abstinence from sexual activity and the effectiveness of other contraceptive methods.

LESSON 2
Identify different types of sexual orientation and explore reasons for other sexual urges.

LESSON 3
Analyze issues surrounding sexual abuse and incest and explore healthy strategies that prevent physical, sexual, and emotional abuse.

Activating Prior Knowledge

Using Visuals Ask Students: How might having the correct information on sexuality benefit teens? Have students write a paragraph about one situation in which having the correct facts would be important.

LESSON 1
Contraception

FOCUS

BIG IDEA It is important for teens to make responsible choices about sexual behavior.

Have students share pregnancy prevention methods they noted for the Motivator. Ask class members if each of the methods mentioned is a myth or a proven scientific method. Explain that in this lesson students will examine different methods of pregnancy prevention

Reading Strategy

Predict Students' questions will vary.

QUICKWRITE

Before students answer, write the following on the board for students to answer: *List some methods of pregnancy prevention.* **Accept reasonable responses.**

Student Objectives

- Analyze the importance of abstinence from sexual activity among teens.
- Recognize abstinence as the only 100 percent effective method in preventing pregnancy and STDs, including HIV/AIDS.
- Analyze the effectiveness of contraceptive methods.

TEACH

Health Skill Practice

Accessing Information Ask students to conduct research to find credible websites providing state-specific information on a minor's rights related to access to contraception. Ask students to write a report describing the source of their information and why they believe it to be a credible source. OL

Contraception

• • • • • • • • • • •
BEFORE YOU READ

Predict. Scan the headings, subheadings, and photo captions. Write a list of questions you have about the material in this lesson.

Vocabulary
withdrawal
contraception
fertility awareness methods (FAMs)
condom
spermicide
diaphragm
cervical cap
oral contraceptives
contraceptive injection
vasectomy
tubal ligation
abortion

• • • • • • • • • • •

BIG IDEA It is important for teens to make responsible choices about sexual behavior.

QUICK WRITE

How much do you know about contraception and STD prevention? *Write down three contraceptive methods that you believe also offer protection against STDs.*

Contraception and Pregnancy Prevention

Each state in the U.S. has different laws related to teens and sexuality. Teens who are sexually active, or who are considering becoming sexually active, should know the laws in their state. These laws cover topics such as the age at which a teen can legally consent to become sexually active, a teen's rights regarding access to contraception, whether the information a teen shares with a doctor is confidential, and also about safe surrender laws, adoption, abortion, and parenting.

For example, how much do you know about contraception and STD prevention? In the United States, approximately 750,000 teens become pregnant each year. Most of these pregnancies are unintended. Some factors that may result in teen pregnancy include:

- **Lack of accurate information.** Some teens do not have access to accurate information regarding contraception and how to avoid an unintended pregnancy.

- **Belief of inaccurate information.** Some myths related to sexuality, contraception, and unplanned pregnancy are believed by many. Believing inaccurate information can lead to an unintended pregnancy.

- **Alcohol and drug use that weaken inhibitions.** After using alcohol or other drugs, some teens may behave in ways that they normally would not.

- **Negative peer pressure.** Peers may try to convince you that becoming sexually active is normal for teens your age. More than half of all teens do not become sexually active until they finish high school.

- **Portrayals of risk-free sex in the media.** The media makes sexual activity look as if it has no consequences. The consequences of becoming sexually active include having an unintended pregnancy and acquiring one or more STDs.

Facts About Pregnancy Prevention

Pregnancy is possible whenever sperm are in or near the opening of the vagina at the same that an ovum is present in a fallopian tube. It is difficult even for mature women to know exactly when ovulation occurs each cycle. In addition, sperm can live for three to six days in the female reproductive tract. Because there is no reliable way for an adolescent to know when ovulation is going to occur, the risk of pregnancy is always present. Here are some important facts about pregnancy and pregnancy prevention:

- Females can ovulate before their first menstrual period, so a teen can become pregnant before menstruation even starts.

- Sperm normally live for 12 to 48 hours inside the female reproductive tract, but they can live for as long as six days.

- Because the timing of ovulation varies and sperm can live inside the female reproductive tract for several days, fertilization is possible even if sexual intercourse occurs during the female's menstrual period.

- It takes only one sperm and one ovum for pregnancy to occur, and any act of sexual intercourse—even the first—can result in pregnancy.

- Sperm cannot be flushed out of the vagina by urinating; urine leaves the body through the urethra, not the vagina.

- Sperm cannot be flushed out of the vagina by douching; in fact, douching may push sperm farther into the vagina, making fertilization more likely.

- Pregnancy can occur even if sexual intercourse occurs while standing up, in a hot tub, or just for a few minutes.

Withdrawal, which is the male's removal of the penis from the vagina before ejaculation, is *not* a reliable method of preventing pregnancy. Some sperm from the ejaculatory duct may be present in the clear fluid released by the Cowper's glands before ejaculation. The male does not know when this pre-ejaculate fluid is being released. Also, if semen is deposited near the outside of the vagina, sperm can travel through vaginal secretions into the vagina. In addition, withdrawing at the height of sexual pleasure requires a great deal of control at a time when the ability to think clearly and act responsibly is strained.

Couples must receive special training from a health care professional to learn how to use FAMs as a form of contraception. **Why is this method not recommended for teens?**

Contraception 77

Critical Thinking

Discussing Discuss why misconceptions about pregnancy prevention are so common. Discuss the bulleted list in the "Facts About Pregnancy Prevention" section and ask students why some people might believe the opposite of these are true. OL

Reliable Sources Ask students for examples of reliable and unreliable sources of information about contraception. Discuss how students can be certain they have correct information. OL

Writing Support

Birth Control Ask students to research the history of one form of birth control discussed in this lesson. Ask them to find out where and when it was first used and how it has changed over the years. Have students write a paragraph summarizing their findings. AL

Caption Answer: *A female teen's menstrual cycle is usually irregular, which makes it nearly impossible to determine when she ovulates.*

Contraception

Active Learning

Class Activity Ask students to list the advantages and disadvantages of the various forms of birth control discussed in this lesson. OL

Critical Thinking

Birth Control Options Ask students why some adult couples might choose fertility awareness methods as their form of birth control. OL

Cooperative Learning

Responsibility Divide the class into two groups. Ask each group to decide who is responsible for birth control, the male or the female. Tell the groups to state at least three reasons for their choice. Ask each group to designate a spokesperson to read their answers. Encourage students to discuss the reasons. Finish the activity by telling students that responsible adult couples share responsibility for birth control. AL

Health Skills Practice

Accessing Information Have students research and evaluate the safety and effectiveness of FDA-approved condoms and other contraceptives in preventing HIV, other STDs, and pregnancy. Students should include information on and compare the success and failure rates of each type of contraceptive. Have students organize their results in a table. OL

Contraception

The word **contraception** means prevention of pregnancy. As you read about the various forms of contraception, remember that the only 100 perfect effective method for preventing pregnancy is abstinence from sexual activity. Most birth control methods belong to one of the major contraceptive categories:

- Fertility awareness methods (FAMs)
- Barrier methods
- Hormonal methods
- Permanent methods

Fertility Awareness Methods

Fertility awareness methods (FAMs) are methods of contraception that involve determining the fertile days of the female's menstrual cycle and avoiding intercourse during those days. With typical use, FAMS are about 80 percent effective. Because a teen female's menstrual cycle is usually irregular, it is nearly impossible to determine when she ovulates each cycle. Thus, FAMs are a particularly ineffective form of contraception.

- The basal body temperature method involves the female taking and recording her temperature every morning before getting out of bed. A basal thermometer is used to identify the slight rise in the female's temperature that occurs at ovulation and continues until she gets her period.

- The cervical mucus method requires checking the mucus secretion from the cervix daily and recording changes in its characteristics. Cloudy and sticky for most of the cycle, cervical mucus become clear, slippery, and stringy a few days before ovulation.

With all FAMs, once the timing of ovulation has been determined, a couple will abstain from intercourse from six or seven days before ovulation until about three days after ovulation. FAMs are entirely dependent on the female having an established, regular menstrual cycle. However, these methods of contraception provide no protection against STDs.

Barrier Methods

Barrier methods are contraceptive devices that prevent fertilization by keeping sperm from reaching the egg. The sperm are either physically blocked from entering the uterus or spoiled by a chemical before they can reach the egg. The condom, sponge, diaphragm, and cervical cap are all barrier methods that function by physically blocking the sperm. In contrast, spermicide acts as a chemical barrier.

The Condom. The male **condom** is a thin sheath of latex, plastic, or animal tissue that is placed on the erect penis to catch semen. It is a physical barrier to the passage of sperm into the vagina and toward the ovum. Some condoms are also coated with a **spermicide.** Spermicide is a chemical that kills sperm. Condoms can be purchased at drugstores and supermarkets without any prescription or age requirement. For any condom to be an effective contraceptive, it must be used correctly:

- The condom must be unrolled onto the erect penis before there is any contact with the vagina.
- There must be space between the tip of the penis and the end of the condom to leave room for semen. If there is no space, the condom could break or leak, allowing semen out. Some condoms have a built-in receptacle at the tip.
- As soon as ejaculation occurs, the male must hold the condom in place while removing the penis from the vagina. If the condom is not properly removed, once the penis softens, the condom can slip off and release semen into the vagina.

The female condom is a polyurethane pouch that fits inside the vagina. To be effective, it must be inserted before the penis comes into contact with the vagina. Like the male condom, it is available over-the-counter.

Petroleum jelly or other petroleum-based products should never be used with a latex condom. These products can dissolve latex and weaken the condom. Since heat also destroys latex, such condoms should not be stored in the glove compartment of a car or carried in a wallet for any length of time. They should be stored in a cool, dry place. Condoms should never be reused; they should be used only once and then discarded.

The Sponge. The sponge is a disc-shaped polyurethane device that contains spermicide. It must be placed in the vagina prior to sexual contact and continues to work for up to 24 hours. The sponge must not be removed for at least six hours following sexual activity but should be discarded within 30 hours to prevent toxic shock syndrome. The sponge can be purchased without a prescription.

The Diaphragm and Cervical Cap. The diaphragm and cervical cap are barrier devices that can be obtained only with a prescription. A contraceptive **diaphragm** is a soft latex or silicone cup with a flexible rim that covers the entrance to the cervix. A **cervical cap** is a thimble-shaped, soft latex cup that fits snugly over the cervix. Spermicidal jelly or cream is applied inside both the diaphragm and the cervical cap before insertion.

Diaphragms and cervical caps are barrier methods of contraception because they keep the sperm and ovum apart. Contraceptive implants prevent ovulation. **Why are the diaphragm and cervical cap available only with a prescription?**

Jill Braaten/McGraw-Hill Education

LESSON 1
Contraception

Reading Strategy

Emphasize Tell students that for condoms to be an effective protection against unplanned pregnancy and STDs, it is important to follow the instructions on the package. Explain to students that methods using spermicide and birth control pills cannot prevent transmission of STDs. In order to protect against STDs, such methods must be used in conjunction with the male condom. OL

Critical Thinking

Discuss Emphasize in discussion with students the importance of understanding that many contraceptive methods covered here do not protect against STDs. OL

Caption Answer: *Only a health care professional can prescribe the correct size for a female's body.*

LESSON 1
Contraception

Critical Thinking

Discussing Ask students how practicing abstinence to eliminate concerns about unplanned pregnancy or a sexually transmitted disease might affect a teen's mental and emotional health. OL

Caption Answer: *Others include contraceptive suppositories and contraceptive foams, jellies, and creams.*

Diaphragms and cervical caps come in different sizes. A female needs to have a pelvic examination so that the health care professional can measure her. Then a doctor can prescribe the correct size for her body. She also needs instructions for insertion and removal of the device. A female should be refitted for a diaphragm or a cervical cap if she has delivered a baby, had a miscarriage or an abortion, or either gained or lost more than 15 pounds. The diaphragm or cap must be used correctly every time intercourse takes place:

- **Using the Diaphragm.** The diaphragm must be placed in the vagina prior to sexual activity and left in for at least six hours after. If intercourse is repeated, more spermicide must be inserted into the vagina without removing the diaphragm. It can be left in the vagina for up to 24 hours, but leaving it in place longer increases the chance of toxic shock syndrome.

- **Using the Cervical Cap.** Before inserting the cervical cap, the inside of the cup must be one-third full of spermicide. It is important to check that the cervix is completely covered. The cap must stay in place for at least six hours after intercourse, but never for longer than 48 hours.

Spermicide. Contraceptive foams, jellies, creams, and tablets are non-prescriptive forms of birth control that contain a spermicide. The instructions for each type of spermicide vary, but most are applied by inserting an applicator deep into the vagina, near the cervix. To be effective, the spermicide must be applied between 5 and 90 minutes before intercourse. After intercourse, it is important that the female not bathe or douche; the spermicide must remain in place for six to eight hours to be effective.

Condoms are one nonprescription method of contraception. **What are some other barrier methods that are available without a prescription?**

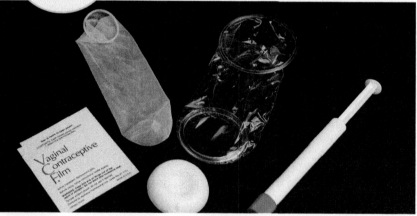

80 Issues of Sexuality

Hormonal Methods

Hormonal methods of contraception function by suppressing ovulation and preventing fertilization or implantation. Such methods include oral contraceptives, patches, vaginal contraceptive rings, and contraceptive injections and implants.

The Birth Control Pill. Oral contraceptives, or birth control pills, are hormone pills that, when taken correctly, create changes in the female body that prevent pregnancy. They are not available over-the-counter. A female must visit a health care professional to obtain a prescription for birth control pills. She will be asked to provide a personal and family medical history. If the doctor feels that a female can safely take the pill, she will receive a prescription and complete instructions.

The pills most often prescribed contain synthetic versions of estrogen and progesterone—two hormones normally produced by the ovaries. The pill must be taken every day to be effective. With correct use, which means that no pills are ever missed, the pill is 99.9 percent effective. If a female misses a dose, she should use another method of birth control. Certain medicines also decrease the effectiveness of the pill.

Although much has been written about the pill and its side effects, these vary for each individual. Some side effects include:

- Nausea
- Breast tenderness
- Weight gain
- Mood swings
- Changes in their menstrual cycle, especially for the first few months
- High blood pressure
- Blood clots
- Stroke

For this reason, females taking birth control pills should have regular medical checkups. They should also notify a physician if any problem or unusual change occurs. Some females, such as those who experience migraine headaches or have diabetes or high blood pressure, should not take the pill. The pill is also not recommended for females who smoke or are severely overweight.

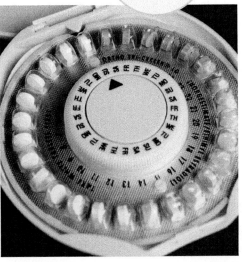

To be effective, birth control pills must be taken every day, preferably at the same time of day. **How effective are birth control pills if taken correctly?**

Christopher Kerrigan/McGraw-Hill Education

Contraception **81**

Reading Strategy

Emphasize Along with being an effective form of birth control, the pill may provide some protection against ovarian and endometrial cancers. Women who use the pill have fewer ectopic pregnancies. OL

Caption Answer: *99 percent effective.*

LESSON 1
Contraception

Reading Strategy

Building Vocabulary Ask students to look up the root *–ectomy* ("surgical removal") and the word *ligation* ("something that binds or is tied") in the dictionary. Then ask them what they think the terms *vasectomy* and *tubal ligation* mean. AL

Critical Thinking

Permanent Methods Tell students that reversing a vasectomy or tubal ligation is expensive, and success cannot be guaranteed. Ask students why people might want to reverse such procedures. OL

The Patch. The patch is a hormonal contraceptive method that works by releasing estrogen and progestin to stop ovulation. It is only available by prescription. The patch can be worn on the lower abdomen, buttocks, or upper body and must be replaced every week for three weeks each month. Using the patch carries a greater risk for blood clots than using oral contraceptives, because the patch has higher levels of estrogen.

Vaginal Contraceptive Ring. The vaginal contraceptive ring is another prescribed hormonal contraceptive method that releases progestin and estrogen to stop ovulation. It is a flexible ring that is put into the vagina and left in place for three weeks of every cycle. It is removed during the menstrual period. Another form of birth control should be used if the ring remains out of position for more than three hours. It is effective only if it has been in place for seven consecutive days. Side effects and risks are similar to those of oral contraceptives, but may also include vaginal discharge, swelling, and irritation.

Contraceptive Injection. The **contraceptive injection** is a birth control procedure in which a female receives an injection once every three months to prevent ovulation. The shot contains the hormone progestin, which stops ovulation in most women. The first injection is generally given during a menstrual cycle or a few days after a menstrual cycle has started. Using this prescribed form of birth control results in high levels of progesterone in the body. Those who use this method for more than two years may experience bone loss. Other risks include breakthrough bleeding, weight gain, breast tenderness, and headaches.

Contraceptive Implants. In a contraceptive implant, a thin rod is placed under the skin on the upper arm by a nurse or doctor. The rod releases the hormone progestin, which thickens the cervical mucus and prevents sperm from fertilizing the egg. It can also work by preventing ovulation altogether. This device can last up to three years. However, it is not recommended for women who are overweight or taking medication for tuberculosis, seizures, depression, hair loss, nausea, and changes in the menstrual cycle.

Emergency Contraceptive. Pregnancy does not occur immediately after two people engage in sexual activity. In fact, sperm can live inside the body for up to six days waiting for an egg to fertilize. An emergency contraceptive pill can be taken up to 120 hours after having unprotected sex. The pill prevents contraception from occurring. Using the pill does not act as a barrier against the spread of STDs and HIV. Use of emergency contraceptives is controversial. In some states, access to emergency contraceptives is limited to people over the age of 18.

Permanent Methods

Permanent contraceptive methods involve a surgical procedure that makes a male or female incapable of reproducing. These methods include vasectomy and tubal ligation.

REAL WORLD CONNECTION

Health Information from Charts and Graphs

You can get useful information from charts and graphs when you know how to read them. The chart below is based on information available from the Food and Drug Administration (FDA). What type of information does this chart give you? Read all the legends and keys to get the maximum information from the chart.

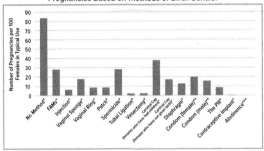

Pregnancies Based on Methods of Birth Control

Source: CDC. Effectiveness of contraceptive methods, www.cdc.gov/reproductive health/
Unintended Pregnancy/Contraception.html

Key:
*   No protection against STDs
** Some protection against STDs
*** Total protection against STDs

Activity: Statistics

Based on the information in the chart, write a summary of the birth control methods covered. In your summary:

- Group methods with similar levels of effectiveness.
- Address the effectiveness of methods that do not fall into any specific group.
- Identify which method is the least effective, which is the most effective, and which offers the most protection against STDs.

Vasectomy. A **vasectomy** is a sterilization procedure for males in which each vas deferens is cut and sealed. It is a method of permanent birth control that works by keeping sperm out of the semen. Sperm are still produced but they are absorbed by the body rather than mixed into the semen. Because sperm are already present in the ducts beyond the points where the vas deferens is cut, vasectomy is not immediately effective. Normally, a male's semen will not be totally free of sperm until 15 to 20 ejaculations have occurred after surgery. Another birth control method must be used to prevent pregnancy until the semen is totally free of sperm. A semen analysis can show whether or not sperm are present.

Contraception **83**

REAL WORLD CONNECTION

Health Information From Charts and Graphs
Summaries should recap birth control methods discussed in the module. Methods should be grouped by their effectiveness of protection against STDs and pregnancy. Remind students that abstinence is the only methods for total protection against STDs and pregnancy. OL

Caption Answer: *A couple may decide they want to have a child or add to their existing family.*

Vasectomy does not in any way affect masculinity or the ability to have an erection, to ejaculate, or to experience sexual pleasure. The procedure is 99.9 perfect effective. However, the surgery does carry some risks, such as pain, bleeding, and infection. Males who may want to have children someday should not have a vasectomy. Surgery to reverse the procedure is costly and has limited success. Vasectomy does not protect the male or female from STDs.

Tubal Ligation. A **tubal ligation** is a sterilization procedure for females in which the fallopian tubes are cut and tied or clamped. This prevents sperm from reaching the ova. An ovum is still released each month, but it cannot be fertilized and dissolves inside the body. Tubal ligation is a more involved procedure than vasectomy and requires a hospital stay. Complications following surgery may include cramps, heavier periods, breakthrough bleeding, and pelvic pain. Tubal ligation is 99.5 percent effective and is considered permanent. Surgery to reverse the procedure has met with limited success in restoring fertility. As with vasectomy, this method of birth control offers no protection against STDs, including HIV/AIDS.

In a vasectomy, each vas deferens is cut and sealed off. During a tubal ligation, the fallopian tubes are cut and tied or clamped off to prevent sperm from reaching the ova. **Why might a couple want to have a vasectomy procedure reversed?**

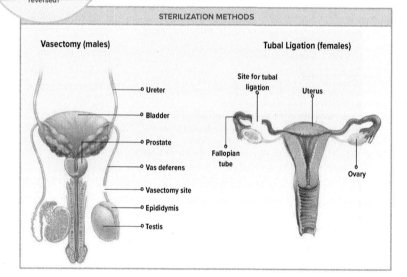

STERILIZATION METHODS

Vasectomy (males)

- Ureter
- Bladder
- Prostate
- Vas deferens
- Vasectomy site
- Epididymis
- Testis

Tubal Ligation (females)

Site for tubal ligation

Uterus

Fallopian tube

Ovary

Pregnancy Termination

Pregnancies end prematurely for many reasons. Any termination of a pregnancy is called an **abortion.** When a pregnancy ends spontaneously from natural causes, it is called a spontaneous abortion or miscarriage. Miscarriages are most common in the first trimester of a pregnancy. It is estimated that as many as 25 percent of all pregnancies end in miscarriage, many without the females even knowing they had been pregnant. Miscarriage may occur for a variety of reasons, including a hormonal deficiency, a faulty ovum or sperm, or a weak endometrium. When miscarriage occurs, it is usually early in the pregnancy and is something over which the female has little or no control.

A medically terminated pregnancy, also called an induced abortion, purposely ends a pregnancy. Although an induced abortion is generally safe, it is a surgery and carries the same risk as all surgeries. An induced abortion is a medical procedure and must be performed by qualified professionals in a medical setting. In addition, laws about terminating pregnancy differ from state to state. The issue of induced abortion is highly controversial and should never be considered a method of birth control. Each state has its own laws related to the age of a person requesting an abortion. States also decide whether a young person can keep an abortion confidential, or if parental consent is required for a minor to obtain an induced abortion.

Abstinence

Abstinence from sexual activity is the only 100 percent effective method for preventing pregnancy and STDs. By making a decision to abstain from sexual activity, you demonstrate maturity and a positive self-concept, and you preserve your chances of fulfilling your goals for the future.

Q&A

Which types of male condoms protect against STDs?

Latex condoms offer the best protection against most STDs, including HIV infection. When used correctly—before there is any sexual contact—they block the exchange of body fluids that may be infected with the pathogens that cause STDs. Polyurethane condoms are also effective, but they are still being studied. Animal tissue condoms do not offer effective protection against STDs because natural pores in the tissue allow passage of some infectious agents, including HIV. Keep in mind that condoms must be used each and every time sexual intercourse takes place, and instructions must be followed exactly.

Lesson 1 Review

Facts and Vocabulary

1. Name two hormonal methods of contraception and explain how each works.

2. Explain the proper way to use a male condom.

3. List four possible side effects of the birth control pill.

4. Explain how barrier methods of contraception work. Identify one method that is designed for males and one that is designed for females.

Thinking Critically

5. **Analyze.** Using a scale of 1 to 5 (with 1 being the most effective), analyze the effectiveness and ineffectiveness of each of the following contraceptive methods in preventing pregnancy: diaphragm, birth control pill, spermicide, abstinence, male condom.

6. **Synthesize.** Analyze the effectiveness and ineffectiveness of the following contraceptive methods in preventing STDs: diaphragm, birth control pill, FAMs, abstinence, condom.

Applying Health Skills

7. **Advocacy.** Create a concept for a poster that compares various methods of contraception and shows why abstinence from sexual activity is the only birth control method that is 100 percent effective in preventing pregnancy and STDs, including HIV/AIDS.

ASSESS

Reteaching Have students make a chart of prescription and nonprescription contraceptive methods.

Enrichment Have students prepare speeches advocating abstinence for their peers.

Sum up the lesson by asking students to explain the role of abstinence in avoiding pregnancy or STDs. Remind students that abstinence is the only 100 percent effective method to prevent pregnancy.

Lesson 1 Review Answers

1. Any of the following: oral contraceptive, patches, vaginal contraceptive rings, and contraceptive injections and implants. Answers should go on to explain in more detail any two of the hormonal contraceptive methods.

2. The male condom must be unrolled onto the erect penis, keeping a space between the tip of the penis and the end of the condom, before there's any contact with the vagina. As soon as ejaculation occurs, and while holding the condom in place, the penis must be removed from the vagina. Condoms must never be used with petroleum-based products, stored in a hot place, or reused.

3. Any four of the following: nausea, breast tenderness, weight gain, mood swings, breakthrough bleeding.

4. Barrier methods prevent fertilization by blocking sperm from reaching the egg. For males: the condom; for females: the sponge, diaphragm, cervical cap, or female condom.

5. 1) abstinence 2) the pill 3) male condom 4) diaphragm 5) spermicide.

6. Only abstinence offers total protection against STDs; condoms provide some protection.

7. Posters will vary.

LESSON 2
Concerns About Sexuality

FOCUS

BIG IDEA Understanding sexual feelings is an important part of physical, mental/emotional, and social health.

Explain to students that in this lesson, they will learn about masturbation, sexual orientation, and abortion.

Reading Strategy

Vocabulary Cards Students' vocabulary cards should reflect their current knowledge of the lesson.

QUICKWRITE

Before students answer, write the following on the board for students to answer: *List two myths about human sexuality issues.*

Student Objectives:

- Explain why some people masturbate.
- Describe myths regarding sexual orientation.
- Distinguish between spontaneous and induced abortion.

TEACH

Critical Thinking

Discussion Ask students why some people have claimed that masturbation has harmful effects. Ask students for reasons why some people might think masturbation is inappropriate. OL

Reading Strategy

Building Vocabulary Have students look up the vocabulary words in the dictionary and compare the meanings with those found in the Glossary/Glosario. BL EL

Concerns About Sexuality

BEFORE YOU READ

Explain. Write down the Building Vocabulary terms and include a definition for each in your own words. After reading the lesson, compare your definitions to those in the text.

Vocabulary

masturbation
homosexual
bisexual
heterosexual
transgender
intersexual
questioning
stereotype

BIG IDEA Understanding sexual feelings is an important part of physical, mental/emotional, and social health.

QUICK WRITE

Write a list of questions you have about sexuality. After reading the lesson, review your list and consider talking to a trusted adult about any remaining questions or concerns.

Recognizing Sexual Feelings

Some people find discussing sexual issues uncomfortable and therefore avoid such discussions. However, lack of accurate information can cause unnecessary concern and confusion. Reluctance to get the facts may lead to misunderstandings that can have a significant impact on health. Knowing the facts not only will help you understand your growth and development, but also will help you make decisions that promote your health and protect you from certain diseases and other conditions.

Masturbation

Some people believe that **masturbation** is a natural part of growth and development, while others believe it is wrong and unhealthy. Masturbation means touching one's own genitals for sexual pleasure. People masturbate to relieve sexual tension. For some people, masturbation is a responsible alternative to sexual intercourse. This is because it relieves sexual tension but poses no risk of pregnancy or contracting STDs. Other people choose not to masturbate for a variety of reasons, including religious beliefs.

Masturbation is a personal issue and a private activity. It should not affect a person's social growth or ability to make friends. Problems can arise, however, with any behavior that becomes obsessive (extremely habitual) or interferes with other areas of a person's life. There may be psychological stress if people feel guilty about what they are doing, or if they find it difficult to think about or focus on other people and activities.

Sexual Orientation

Sexual orientation is part of a person's personality. It is the way people view themselves and their attraction to others. People use many different labels to describe their sexual orientation and gender identity. A few of the most common are:

- **Homosexual** describes an individual who is romantically and sexually attracted to people of the same gender.
- **Bisexual** describes an individual who is romantically and sexually attracted to people of both genders.
- **Heterosexual** describes an individual who is attracted to people of the opposite gender.
- **Transgender** describes individuals whose gender identity differs from others of their gender. They can be heterosexual, homosexual, or bisexual. A transgender person may choose to live as his or her opposite gender.
- **Intersexual** describes an individual who was born with both male and female characteristics.
- **Questioning** describes an individual who questions their own identity and orientation.
- **LGBTQ+** is a common acronym meaning lesbian, gay, bisexual, transgender, or questioning.

About four percent of all Americans identify themselves as being a member of the LGBTQ+ community. This statistic is according to a 2017 study released by Gallup. According to an analysis of the study, the percentage of people identifying themselves as LGBTQ+ will rise. Young people today are more open about issues of sexuality. Many more teens identify themselves as being a member of the LGBTQ+ community. In the future, it is expected that 1 in 10 Americans identify themselves as LGBTQ+. Sexual identity and other issues of sexuality will receive increasingly more attention in the U.S. Some terms used to discuss LGBTQ+ issues include:

- **Gender identity** describes an individual's sense of being male or female.
- **Coming out** describes the process of telling people about one's homosexuality.
- **Homophobia** describes an irrational fear, prejudice, or discrimination towards homosexuals. Homophobia is most often based on fear and ignorance.

What causes sexual orientation? Almost certainly there is no single reason why some people are homosexual, heterosexual, or bisexual. According to the American Psychological Association, sexual orientation is the result of an interaction of cognitive, environmental, and biological factors.

Some people avoid discussing sexual issues, but a lack of accurate information can cause unnecessary concern and confusion. **Why is it so important for teens to get the facts about uncomfortable sexual topics?**

Concerns About Sexuality **87**

Health Skills Practice

Decision Making Have students use the decision-making process to analyze the benefits of respecting individual differences in physical appearance, gender roles, and sexual orientation. Have students record their responses in their health journals. OL

Cultural Awareness

Stereotypes Have students discuss why stereotypes are damaging. OL

Critical Thinking

Discussing Ask students what they would say to a friend who thinks he or she might be gay because he or she is not interested in members of the opposite gender. AL

Caption Answer: *Knowing the facts about sexual issues can help teens make informed decisions that promote health and protect them from diseases.*

Concerns About Sexuality

Health Skill Practice

Accessing Information Ask students to conduct research to find credible websites providing state-specific information on a minor's rights related to access to pregnancy, safe surrender laws (also called safe haven laws), induced abortion, adoption, and parenting. Ask students to write a report describing the source of their information and why they believe it to be a credible source. OL

Active Learning

Class Discussion Have students work in small groups to brainstorm examples in which someone they know or someone they consider a role model demonstrated respect for others, appreciated diversity, showed empathy, or appreciated a different perspective. Then have groups share their examples with the class. Have a short discussion on why it is important to demonstrate these traits. OL

Teens who identify as LGBTQ+ experience stress. Concerns may include how family and friends will accept the teens' status to fears about being teased or even attacked. Some teens may believe they are the only person with LGBTQ+ feelings. This belief can lead them to feel isolated and depressed. It can be helpful for adolescents who have questions related to sexuality to contact the GLBT National Help Center. Factual information can help teens who are handling issues related to sexuality.

Myths About Homosexuality

There are many myths about homosexuality. The idea that all homosexuals, bisexuals, or heterosexuals act in one particular way is based on **stereotypes.** A stereotype is an idea or image held about a group of people that represents a prejudiced attitude, oversimplified opinion, or uninformed judgment. Many of these stereotypes and myths can be hurtful to people of all orientations. Some myths include:

- A person is homosexual because he or she is not yet interested in the opposite gender. (This is not true. A person may develop an interest in the opposite gender much earlier or much later than his or her friends.)

- A person is homosexual just because his or her closest friend is the same gender. (It is not only normal, but also healthy, to have close, caring friendships with peers of the same gender.)

- Someone who has not yet had sexual contact—especially if the person is male—is homosexual. (This is untrue. Having or not having sexual contact has nothing to do with sexual orientation.)

- Homosexuals, bisexuals, or heterosexuals can be identified by their appearance and mannerisms. (This is untrue. Homosexuals, bisexuals, and heterosexuals are all individuals who cannot be identified by the way they dress or act.)

Internal and External Influences

How anyone feels about his or her sexuality is influenced by internal and external factors. Internal factors include the teen's likes and dislikes. External factors include people in the teen's life, the media, and others in the community. External influences can impact how a teen feels and acts. An individual or group can influence how others feel about being LGBTQ+ or whether they are accepting of someone who identifies as being LGBTQ+.

Another external influence comes from families. We learn about relationships by watching our parents or guardians in their relationships. Cultural background affects how a person feels about and expresses gender role, gender identity, and sexual orientation. In some cultures, males are seen as the leaders and females are viewed as nurturers who stay home and care for the family. Some cultures believe in strict gender roles. In these cultures, anyone who does not follow the customary norms for sexual behavior might be threatened. Even in a relatively open society, such as the United States, some LBGTQ individuals live in fear and feel that they must hide their sexual orientation.

Today many cultures are becoming more tolerant. They are beginning to accept that gender roles are changing within societies. They are beginning to accept that some people identify with the opposite gender, and that transgender people may take steps to live as a member of the opposite gender. The acceptance of people who are attracted to members of the same gender is also accepted to a greater degree than it has been in the past.

Respecting Differences

Individuals should not be stereotyped based on their appearance or sexual orientation. It is important to remember that every person is unique and worthy of consideration and respect as an individual. People should be respected for their differences and sexual orientation, and not face harassment or violence due to homophobia.

Many homosexual teens are accepted by their friends, families, and communities. However, some gay teens feel the need to hide their sexual orientation. They fear discrimination and rejection from their friends and family, which can lead to emotional problems such as anxiety and depression. Some homosexual teens without support systems may be at a higher risk than heterosexual teens for dropping out of school, drug and alcohol abuse, and suicide.

Coming Out

The term *coming out* refers to recognizing that you are LGBTQ+ and telling others. Some people who are LGBTQ+ report that they began feeling different at an early age. Other people may not be aware of having these feelings until later in life. When a person recognizes that he or she is LGBTQ+, the person has come out to oneself. When a person tells others that he or she identifies as being LGBTQ+, he or she is coming out to others.

Coming out is a difficult decision. Many people worry about how their family and friends will react to the information. For this reason, the individual who is experiencing these feelings is the only person who can decide who to tell and when to tell others. No one should pressure someone to come out before he or she is ready. Coming out is a personal decision.

A person who decides to come out should carefully consider how to share the information. The person should think about his or her relationship with the other person. How can these feelings be shared in a loving, nonjudgmental way? A person who is deciding about coming out should consider these tips before coming out.

- Define the reasons to come out.
- Avoid coming out when angry.
- Avoid coming out to someone who may cause physically harm.
- Avoid telling bullies or someone who will tell others without permission.

Many myths exist about homosexuality. **Why are stereotypes damaging?**

Concerns About Sexuality

Critical Thinking

Discussion Ask students to think about the effects a termination of pregnancy might have on a female. Ask Students: *How can this decision affect physical, mental, and social health*? OL

Controversial Topics Remind students that induced abortion is a highly debated subject in the United States, and that laws regarding abortion differ from state to state. Have students discuss why induced abortion is a controversial subject. OL AL

Cultural Awareness

Research Ask students to find articles relating to an election campaign where the candidate discusses his or her views of abortion. Have them summarize the politician's views and explain why politicians often state their views on abortion. AL

Caption Answer: *Stereotyping individuals based on prejudices or opinions can damage a person's self esteem and overall emotional health.*

LESSON 2
Concerns About Sexuality

ASSESS

Reteaching Ask students to summarize why they think each of the subjects in this lesson is the controversial.

Enrichment Have students select an option for dealing with an unplanned pregnancy. Students should research this option and write a paper that describes its impact and what should be considered. If appropriate, have volunteers share their papers with the class.

Sum up the lesson by stating that there are many controversial issues surrounding the topic of sexuality, and everyone needs not agree.

Caption Answer: *Sexual orientation is the recognition of a gender preference with regard to sexual attraction.*

Throughout the life cycle, it is normal and healthy to have close friendships with peers of the same gender. Such friendships have no bearing on sexual orientation. **What is sexual orientation?**

Character Check

When you show empathy and tolerance for people who are different from you, you are demonstrating respect. Imagine you overhear your brother telling a friend that someone is homosexual. You are concerned that your brother is stereotyping. Write what you would say to him.

A person who has come out should be prepared for the possibility that the other person may initially deny what is said. The person hearing the information may be surprised and say things that he or she later regrets. Remember that some people may have their own ideas about another person's gender identity or sexual orientation. The disclosure may change that idea and the person may feel surprised by the announcement.

Teens who are struggling with coming out have a resource that can provide help and advice. The Trevor Project operates a free, 24-hour, 7-day-a-week hotline (1-866-488-7386) for LGBTQ+ youth. Staff who take calls are trained to help people who are struggling with coming out, or who are considering suicide. All calls are confidential, which means that no one will know that you called or what you talked about to the counselor.

Dating

Dating is a way to get to know other people better. For a LGBTQ+ teen, though, dating can be very difficult. LGBTQ+ teens who are open about their orientation may have difficulty finding other teens in their school to date. A community with a youth organization for LGBTQ+ teens may be a place to connect with other teens.

Declining a Date

Asking a person out on a date can be a very difficult experience. A person who is known for a long time may be a good person to ask on a date, but if that person wants to be only friends, he or she may decline the date. For LGBTQ+ teens, dating can be even more difficult. Some teens may feel threatened by the sexual orientation of an LGBTQ+ teen. Other may feel that they are LGBTQ+ as well, but are not ready to come out. In these instances, your goal should be to decline the date, but maintain the friendship. Be respectful. Tell the other person no, but that you want to remain friends. If you feel comfortable, tell the person why you are saying no.

Lesson 2 Review

Facts and Vocabulary

1. Define the terms *homosexual*, *bisexual*, and *heterosexual*.

2. What is a stereotype?

3. What are some myths about sexual orientation? Explain why they are unfounded.

Thinking Critically

4. **Analyze.** Why can stereotypes harm people?

5. **Synthesize.** What are some internal and external factors that influence an LGBTQ+ individual's health?

Applying Health Skills

6. **Communication Skills.** Write a paragraph explaining what you would say to a friend who tells you that she is concerned about her sexual orientation because she has not started dating yet.

Lesson 2 Review Answers

1. A homosexual is someone who is sexually attracted to people of the same gender. A heterosexual is someone who is sexually attracted to people of the opposite gender. A bisexual person is attracted to people of both genders.

2. A stereotype is an idea or image held about a group of people that represents a prejudiced attitude, an oversimplifi ed opinion, or uninformed judgment.

3. Answers will vary, but could include the following: A person is homosexual because he or she is not yet interested in the opposite gender, because his or her closest friend is of the same gender, or because he or she has not yet had sexual contact—especially if the person is male.

4. Possible answer: Stereotypes can harm people because they are based on the way people look or behave, and they result in people being incorrectly labeled instead of being shown consideration and respect.

5. Possible Answer: Internal factors include personal likes and dislikes. External factors include people in the person's life, the media, and others in the community.

6. Paragraphs will differ but should reflect an understanding of myths and stereotypes surrounding homosexuality.

Sexual Abuse and Violence

BIG IDEA Sexual activity can have serious consequences on a teen's life.

Sexual Abuse and Incest

Whenever any act of sexual contact is forced on a person, it is an act of violence. Although in some cases a stranger attacks a person and forces sexual contract on him or her, more often the attacker is someone the victim knows. The force used against the victim may be physical, but when the attacker is familiar to the victim, the force is likely to be psychological and emotional as well.

Abuse can take many forms. It can be physical, sexual, or emotional, or a combination of all or any of those three.

- Physical abuse is any sort of action that causes physical injury or pain. It can include hitting, burning, biting, choking, and beating, among others.
- Sexual abuse is any type of sexual contact between an adult and a person younger than 18, an older child and younger child, or when one person forces another person to have unwanted sexual contact.
- Emotional abuse is any type of abuse where a person's self-esteem and feelings of self-worth are damaged. It can include threats, criticism, and yelling.

Sexual abuse is any sexual contact that is physically or emotionally forced on a person against his or her will. Sexual abuse is always illegal, it is always a crime, and it is never the victim's fault. It can affect people of all social, economic, and ethnic groups. Males and females of any age may be victims of sexual abuse.

Children and teens who are victims of sexual abuse frequently know their abuser as someone they trust. Such a person takes advantage of the young victim's trust and uses his or her position of authority to pressure the victim into sexual activity.

BEFORE YOU READ

Predict. Scan the headings, subheadings, and photo captions. Write a list of questions you have about the material in this lesson.

Vocabulary
sexual abuse
incest
sexual harassment
rape
acquaintance rape
date rape

Sexual Abuse and Violence

FOCUS

BIG IDEA Sexual activity can have serious consequences on a teen's life.

Explain that people sometimes think that rape only happens between strangers or that you can identify a rapist by the way he looks. Tell them that in this lesson, they will learn that rape is any forced sexual contact.

Reading Strategy

Predict Students' questions will vary.

QUICKWRITE

Before students answer, write the following on the board for students to answer: *What associations come to mind when you see or hear the word rape? Do you know why you have these associations?* **Accept reasonable responses.**

Student Objectives:

- Analyze issues surrounding sexual abuse and incest.
- Describe situations that can lead to acquaintance rape and date rape.
- Analyze the importance of healthy strategies that prevent physical, sexual, and emotional abuse.

TEACH

Reading Strategy

Building Vocabulary Point out to students that there are three vocabulary terms in this lesson using the word *rape*. Ask them to write what they think are the differences between the three words and then check the Glossary/Glosario to see how the terms are defined. OL

Active Learning

Help for Victims Have students put together a list of local agencies that assist victims of sexual assault, sexual abuse, and incest. Provide each student with a copy of the list and make sure students understand the function of each agency. OL

LESSON 3
Sexual Abuse and Violence

Critical Thinking

Protecting Yourself Males often think that they cannot be sexually assaulted. Discuss whether sexual assault is a problem that victimizes both males and females. What can young people do to protect themselves from sexual assault? OL

Active Learning

Guest Speaker Invite a speaker from a rape crisis center to speak to the class. Before the speaker's visit, have the class make a list of questions they want to ask. OL

Critical Thinking

Finding Help Ask students what they should do if they suspected a friend was being sexually abused. Ask students to discuss why a victim of sexual abuse may find it difficult to report the crime. Ask students why it is important for both the abuser and the victim to get help. AL OL

Active Learning

Laws Related to Sexting Tell students that there are many reasons not to *sext*. Sending text messages, pictures, or other sexually-graphic materials is prohibited in many states, especially if this material is unwanted or sent without permission. Help students find laws that their state or local governments have passed regarding these activities and their consequences. AL

If the sexual abuser is related to the victim, the abuse is called **incest**. Incest can involve parents or stepparents, aunts, uncles, brothers, sisters, or any other relative. Whenever the sexual abuser is a trusted adult, the pressure used against a young victim is commonly persuasive or emotional rather than physical. The adult may discourage the victim from telling anyone about the abuse by using statements such as:

- "This will be our special secret."
- "You'll break up the family."
- "I'll go to jail and it will be your fault."
- "No one will believe you, and I'll say you're lying."
- "Your parents will be very mad at/disappointed in you."

These types of statements are very persuasive because they can provoke guilt and anxiety in young people. Many victims remain silent about the abuse out of fear, loyalty, or obedience. Some victims may believe they caused the abuse or that they were at fault because they did not resist. Unfortunately, children may not understand or know that nonconsensual sexual contact is wrong. Remember that, without exception, sexual abuse is the fault of the abuser, not the victim.

What to Do About Sexual Abuse

The first and most important step a victim of sexual abuse can take is to tell someone about the abuse. This is particularly difficult to do if the abuser is a family member, a friend of the family, or a leader within the community. People might not believe the victim because they can't imagine that the accused person could be a sexual abuser. If this happens, the victim should keep trying until he or she finds someone who takes the victim seriously.

A victim of abuse can find help from a parent or guardian, a doctor, the school nurse, a school social worker, a guidance counselor, a trusted teacher, a close friend's parent, or the local police. Both the victim and the abuser need professional help and counseling.

Sexual Harassment

Another form of sexual abuse is **sexual harassment**. This is any unwanted or unwelcome sexual contact or communication. This may be targeted at someone or merely take place while someone is present. Victims can feel threatened, pressured, or uncomfortable. Sexual harassment may include jokes, gestures, or physical contact. Sometimes, sexual harassment may escalate to sexual violence, which is any form of unwelcome sexual contact directed at an individual.

Rape

Rape is any form of sexual intercourse that takes place against a person's will. It is illegal. As with other types of sexual abuse, rape is an act of violence, not of passion. Victims of rape can be males or females of any age. In the United States, about 135,000 people were victims of rape crimes in the year 2017. Females account for 90 percent of rape victims, 10 percent of victims are males, and about 44 percent of victims are under the age of 18.

Many rapes of teens are either **acquaintance rape**, which is rape by someone the victim knows, or **date rape**, which is rape by someone the victim is dating. A victim of date or acquaintance rape may think it wasn't rape because he or she knows the attacker, or he or she may feel responsible for a rape because they did not resist soon enough or firmly enough. Whenever any sexual act is forced on a person against his or her will, it is rape, and rape is never the victim's fault.

For many victims, fear that they will be blamed or will not be believed may prevent them from telling anyone about the rape. Because our society gives males the message that they are strong and should be able to protect themselves, a male victim of rape may find discussing the rape especially difficult.

Fear, anger, grief, shame, and embarrassment keep many victims from reporting rape. However, one of the best ways to reduce the occurrence of rape is for all victims to report it. Although the reporting procedure can be difficult, embarrassing, or upsetting, an unreported rape leaves the rapist uncaught, unpunished, and free to rape again.

Reduce Your Risk of Rape

Follow these commonsense guidelines to reduce your risk of rape:

- Do not go places alone; stay with a group.
- If you do go somewhere alone, tell someone your plans.
- Walk briskly, be aware of your surroundings, and look alert.
- Stay in well-lit areas where other people are present.
- Have your keys out and ready as you approach your home or car.

Many rapes of teens are cases of either acquaintance rape or date rape, in which the victim knows the rapist. **What are some factors that might keep a victim from reporting a rape?**

S. Olsson/PhotoAlto

Sexual Abuse and Violence

Health Skills Practice

Accessing Information Have students work in small groups to research more about the laws in your state regarding harassment, acquaintance and statutory rape, and sexual abuse. Have groups summarize the results in a bulleted list and share it with the class. Discuss why it is important to be aware of and understand these laws. OL

Active Learning

Reducing Risk Review the "Reduce Your Risk of Rape" section of the lesson. Ask students to make a list of other ways to protect against rape (for example, to be wary of meeting people on the Internet). Remind students that rape is never the victim's fault. OL

Caption Answer: *Answers will vary but may include such factors as fear, anger, grief, shame, or embarrassment.*

LESSON 3
Sexual Abuse and Violence

Active Learning

Discuss Dealing with the trauma of a sexual assault will take time. Discuss what can be done to help victims of sexual assault recover both physically and emotionally. Ask students to make a list of strategies to show support and caring for someone who has been raped. OL

Writing Support

Research Have students find current articles about rape cases in which the assailant was convicted. Tell students to find out what sentences were given to those found guilty. Have student summarize their findings in a few paragraphs. Have students compare their findings with those of the rest of the class. AL

- Lock all doors and keep windows up when driving; check inside and under a parked car before getting in.
- Keep windows and doors locked at home; never open your door to strangers.
- If you have car trouble, stay inside your locked car. If someone offers to help, remain in your car and ask the person to call for assistance.
- Keep a cell phone in your purse or car.
- If you are being followed, go to a public place. Run, scream, and make as much noise as you can.

Protecting Yourself Against Date Rape

Use these tips to protect yourself against date rape:
- Do not go on blind dates. Know the person you are going out with.
- Go on group dates the first few times you're out with a new person.
- Do not go to isolated places on a date.
- Tell someone at home where you will be and when you plan to return.
- Take money with you, including change, so that you can make a phone call or take a taxi home if a situation becomes unsafe. If you have a cell phone, bring it.
- Do not use drugs or alcohol. If your date is using these substances, leave immediately.

What to Do if You or Someone You Know is Raped

Being raped is a terrifying experience. If you or someone you know has been raped, do the following:
- Tell a parent, close friend, or someone else you trust; ask for emotional support.
- Notify the police immediately. Ask for a sex crimes officer of the same gender as you are.
- Do not take a shower, change clothes, or douche. These actions can remove evidence that the police will need.
- Get a physical examination as soon as possible. Most rape victims have injuries that need medical attention. A hospital emergency room is equipped to handle rape cases and can take semen samples to help identify the rapist. Emergency room personnel may give the victim an antibiotic to fight possible infections and can provide counsel about the possibility of becoming pregnant or contracting an STD or HIV/AIDS.
- Find a counselor, therapist, or support group to help work through the emotional trauma of rape. It is normal for a rape victim to have a wide range of feelings. Talking about fears and concerns is an important way to start healing from the emotional wounds. Many communities have a rape crisis center with counselors who are specially trained for this purpose.

Internet Safety

The Internet is a useful resource, but it can also be a dangerous place. The hazards you can encounter range from upsetting situations, like being insulted in a chat room, to physical threats, such as Internet predators.

When you're online, you need to know how protect yourself. Here are a few precautions to take when you're online:

- **Keep your identity private.** Avoid posting personal information in any public space. This includes your full name, address, phone number, financial information, passwords, the name of your school, and anything else a stranger could use to track you down in the real world.
- **Keep online relationships online.** Agreeing to meet in person with someone you've met online can be risky.
- **Don't respond to inappropriate messages.** If anyone sends you a message that makes you feel uncomfortable for any reason, tell a parent or other trusted adult.
- **Let your parents or guardians know what you're doing online.** Tell them about people you meet online, the same way you'd talk to them about your friends in the real world.
- **Do not post questionable photos.** *Sexting* is the slang term for sending sexually explicit photographs or texts via mobile phones. These images and texts sent in private can easily be distributed and displayed publicly. Posting or distributing sexually explicit photos of a person under 18 years old can also be considered child pornography.

Health Minute

Avoid Becoming a Victim of Date Rape Drugs

The term *date rape drugs* is used to describe the drugs Rohypnol, GHB, and ketamine, which rapists sometimes give to unknowing victims, usually by dissolving the drug in a drink. These drugs cause blackouts and memory loss, leaving a victim helpless, unaware of what is happening, and unable to recall what happened.

To protect yourself against date rape drugs:

- Never accept any kind of drink from someone you don't know well and trust completely.
- Never accept a drink you have not seen poured or made.
- Do not leave your drink unattended.
- Do not accept a drink from a large public beverage container, such as a punch bowl.
- If you feel ill, ask for help immediately and publicly.

Lesson 3 Review

Facts and Vocabulary

1. Define the term *sexual abuse*.

2. Why might a victim of sexual abuse or incest remain silent about the abuse?

3. What is the first and most important step a victim of sexual abuse can take?

4. List three things you can do to protect yourself against date rape.

5. Why shouldn't a victim of rape take a shower or change clothes afterward?

Thinking Critically

6. **Analyze.** What is the difference between sexual abuse and incest?

7. **Synthesize.** List five situations a person could be in that might put him or her at risk of being a victim of rape. Suggest ways this person can make better decisions to protect himself or herself.

Applying Health Skills

8. **Practicing Healthful Behaviors.** Analyze the importance of healthy strategies to prevent physical, sexual, and emotional abuse, including date rape. Create a script for an audio podcast or short video that offers tips for teens on how to protect themselves against rape.

Sexual Abuse and Violence

ASSESS

Reteaching Have students explain the importance of immediately reporting a rape to the authorities.

Enrichment Ask students to research statistics on rape victims. Ask them to find out the percentages of rape victims by gender and age.

Sum up the lesson by asking volunteers to summarize what they have learned about ways young people can protect themselves against sexual abuse.

Lesson 3 Review Answers

1. Sexual abuse is any sexual contact that is physically or emotionally forced on a person.
2. A victim of sexual abuse or incest may remain silent about the abuse out of fear, loyalty, or obedience; some victims may believe that they caused the abuse or that they were at fault because they did not resist.
3. The first and most important step a victim of sexual abuse can take is to tell someone about the abuse.
4. Any three of the following: know the person you are going out with and learn about his or her friends and reputation; do not go on blind dates alone; go on group dates the first few times you're out with a new person; do not go to isolated places on a date; tell someone at home where you will be and when you plan to return; take money with you and a cell phone if you have one; do not use drugs or alcohol, and leave immediately if your date uses them.
5. These actions can remove evidence the police will need.
6. Incest is a specific type of sexual abuse that occurs when the sexual abuser is related to the victim.
7. Situations will vary, but students should include some of the information under the head "Protecting Yourself Against Rape" in their suggestions.
8. Pamphlets will vary but should list and illustrate many of the guidelines discussed in the lesson.

MODULE 6

Assessment Answers

1. Douching may push sperm farther into the vagina, making fertilization more likely.

2. Withdrawal is the male's removal of the penis from the vagina before ejaculation; it is not an effective method of preventing pregnancy.

3. Permanent methods of contraception include the vasectomy and tubal ligation.

4. Two fertility awareness methods of contraception are the basal body temperature method and the cervical mucus method.

5. Prescription forms of birth control include any of the following: birth control pills, diaphragm, cervical cap, or contraceptive implants.

6. Oral contraceptives are hormone pills that, taken correctly, make changes in the female body that prevent pregnancy.

7. A contraceptive implant provides protection from pregnancy for about five years.

8. Spontaneous abortion or miscarriage.

9. Rape is sexual intercourse through force or threat of force.

10. Acquaintance rape is rape by someone the victim knows, whereas date rape is rape by someone the victim is dating.

11. Answers will vary, but students might suggest that they could talk to a trusted adult such as a teacher or a doctor, or they could consult reference material from the library or reliable Internet sites.

12. During a vasectomy, each vas deferens is cut and sealed. The procedure takes about 20 minutes and involves using a local anesthetic. It is not immediately effective; a male's semen will not be totally free of sperm until 15 to 20 ejaculations after surgery. The procedure is 99.9 percent effective. In a tubal ligation, the fallopian tubes are cut and tied or clamped to prevent sperm from reaching the ova. Complications following surgery may include cramps, heavier periods, breakthrough bleeding, and pelvic pain. Tubal ligation is 99.5 percent effective.

13. Answers will vary, but students should include the health consequences of sexual activity before marriage.

14. Answers will vary, but students may say it happens because they trust the people who give them the false information.

15. A counselor can help victims talk about their fears and concerns about the abuse.

16. Students' directories should provide comprehensive contact information.

17. Answers will vary, but will probably include the idea that movie characters might influence teens to engage in high-risk sexual behaviors.

Reviewing Facts and Vocabulary

1. Why is douching not an effective method of contraception?

2. What is *withdrawal*? Is it an effective method of preventing pregnancy?

3. Name two forms of permanent contraception.

4. List two fertility awareness methods of contraception.

5. Name three prescription forms of birth control.

6. What are *oral contraceptives*?

7. How long does a contraceptive implant provide protection from pregnancy?

8. What is the term for a pregnancy that ends spontaneously?

9. What is *rape*?

10. Explain the difference between *acquaintance rape* and *date rape*.

Writing Critically

11. Synthesize. Write a summary describing what you would do if you received conflicting information about contraception. Where would you go to find the correct information?

12. Compare. Write a summary comparing vasectomy and tubal ligation in terms of the actual procedure and effectiveness.

13. Synthesize. Using facts from this module, write an analysis of the importance of abstinence from sexual activity as the preferred choice of behavior for an unmarried person of school age.

14. Analyze. Write a report explaining why you think some people believe false information about sexual issues, such as homosexuality or bisexuality.

15. Evaluate. Write a paragraph describing how a child who has been sexually abused might be helped by a counselor who specializes in such cases.

Applying Health Skills

16. Accessing Information. Create a directory of all the resources available in your community to help people with contraception, STDs, sexual abuse, and rape.

17. Analyzing Influences. How might movies that feature people making unsafe decisions about sexual activity negatively affect a teen audience?

BEYOND THE CLASSROOM ACTIVITIES

PARENT INVOLVEMENT
Discuss Safety Strategies. With a parent or guardian, discuss ways that teens can reduce the risk of date or acquaintance rape.

SCHOOL AND COMMUNITY
Help for Victims. Do research at the library and talk to a counselor about treatment of victims of rape and incest. Write a report about the treatment process and add suggestions that you feel might help victims. Suggest ways that present treatment methods might be improved.

BEYOND THE CLASSROOM

Parent Involvement: Discuss Safety Strategies. Have students talk with a parent or guardian about ways to reduce the risk of date or acquaintance rape.

School and Community: Help For Victims. Direct students to conduct research at the library or online and talk to a counselor about treatment of victims of rape and incest. Then have them write a report about the treatment process and add suggestions that they feel might help victims. Students should suggest ways that present treatment methods might be improved.

- Encourage students to participate in activities that involve parents and the community.
- Discussions should include the information presented in Lesson 3.
- Answers will vary.

MODULE 7	STANDARDS / NOTES	LESSON ASSESSMENT
	Use this space for standards and notes.	Module 7 Assessment Online assessment
LESSON 1 **Common Sexually Transmitted Diseases** **BIG IDEA.** Sexually transmitted diseases are highly communicable infections that are contracted through sexual contact. *(30 MIN.)*		Lesson 1 Review Online assessment
LESSON 2 **Other Sexually Transmitted Diseases** **BIG IDEA.** Sexually transmitted diseases pose serious health risks. *(30 MIN.)*		Lesson 2 Review Online assessment

Key to Abilities   Teaching Strategies and Activities have been coded for ability level and appropriateness.

 Activities for students working above grade level

 Activities for students working below grade level

 Activities for students working on grade level

 Activities for English Learners

Sexually Transmitted Diseases

Module Overview Module 7 focuses on explaining and identifying many common STDs and STIs. It explains methods for reducing the risk of exposure to STDs and identifies the resources available to diagnose and treat infections.

LESSON 1
Identify the relationship between high-risk behaviors and the risk of contracting an STD and analyzing strategies to prevent the spread of STDs.

LESSON 2
Identify strategies to prevent spreading STDs and assess community health services available for prevention and treatment of STDs.

Activating Prior Knowledge

Using Visuals Ask students to list reliable sources of information on STDs or STIs. In addition to medical professionals and pamphlets, what other sources could teens use to find accurate information?

MODULE 7

Sexually Transmitted Diseases

LESSONS

1 Common Sexually Transmitted Diseases

2 Other Sexually Transmitted Diseases

97

Common Sexually Transmitted Diseases

FOCUS

BIG IDEA Sexually transmitted diseases are highly communicable infections that are contracted through sexual contact.

Tell students they will learn more about sexually transmitted diseases, their symptoms, and treatments in this lesson.

Reading Strategy

Problems and Solutions Students' summaries and lists will vary.

> **QUICKWRITE**
>
> Before students answer, write the following on the board for students to answer: *List the common symptoms of STDs.* **Accept reasonable responses.**

Student Objectives:

- Describe the relationship between high-risk behaviors and the risk of contracting an STD.
- Discuss abstinence from sexual activity as the only method that is 100 percent effective in preventing STDs and infections.
- Develop and analyze strategies to prevent the spread of STDs.

TEACH

Critical Thinking

Prevention Explain that the CDC has recently used the term sexually transmitted *infection* in an effort to encourage more people to seek testing treatment for an infection. Ask students why they think STDs are on the rise despite all the information available on how to prevent them. OL

Common Sexually Transmitted Diseases

BEFORE YOU READ

Problems and Solutions. Write a brief summary describing some of the behaviors you think can expose someone to an STD or STI. Add a list of tips to prevent the transmission of these diseases and infections.

Vocabulary

sexually transmitted diseases (STDs)
sexually transmitted infections (STIs)
human papillomavirus (HPV)
genital warts
chlamydia
pelvic inflammatory disease (PID)
gonorrhea
genital herpes

BIG IDEA Sexually transmitted diseases are highly communicable infections that are contracted through sexual contact.

> **QUICK WRITE**
>
> Write down the questions you have about STDs. If your questions are not answered after reading the lesson, talk to a trusted adult about any additional concerns related to this topic.

STDs: Widespread Among Teens

Great strides have been made in controlling the spread of many communicable diseases, but the incidence of sexually transmitted diseases continues to rise. **Sexually transmitted diseases (STDs)**, more commonly known as **sexually transmitted infections (STIs)**, are infections that spread from person to person through sexual contact. There are more than 25 known STDs, many of which are difficult to track because people who have them may not exhibit symptoms. Other cases are not reported because people do not seek treatment due to shame, fear, or ignorance.

An estimated 26 million people contracted one or more STDs in the United States in 2018 alone. Almost half of these new cases involve those between the ages of 15 and 24. Currently in the United States, more than 60 million people have a viral STD, which is incurable. The reasons why these epidemics persist and grow include:

- Many STDs have no symptoms.
- Some STDs have a lengthy delay between infection and the appearance of symptoms.
- Some STDs have symptoms that go away while the disease continues to damage the body.
- Many people remain uneducated about STDs or believe that they are somehow immune.

Sexually active teens can contract STDs by engaging in one or more of the following high-risk behaviors:

- Engaging in any form of unprotected intercourse—including oral, anal, or vaginal sexual contact—without using any barrier protection method such as condoms.

- Using alcohol and other drugs, which can change people's behavior and lower their inhibitions.
- Being sexually active with multiple partners.
- Choosing partners who have a history of intravenous drug use.

Abstinence Can Prevent STDs

Some teens may think that only people who are sexually active get STDs. The truth is that anyone who has sexual contract with an infected person is at risk. Because a person who has an STD does not always show symptoms, sexual activity of any kind with any person is risky. The good news is that STDs can be prevented. Choosing to practice abstinence is a healthy, responsible, and mature decision for teens. Here are some guidelines that teens can follow to avoid risky situations:

- Set limits and communicate them to your date before you go out.
- Stay in public places when you go on dates.
- Use refusal strategies if you are pressured to engage in sexual activity.
- Never use alcohol or illegal drugs.
- Choose friends and dates who practice abstinence.
- When attending parties, pour your own beverages and do not leave them unattended to avoid the risk of date rape drugs.
- Use latex condoms to provide the best protection against most STDs.

Common STDs in the United States

In this lesson, you will learn important facts about some of the most common STDs:

- Human papillomavirus
- Chlamydia
- Gonorrhea
- Genital herpes

Remember, the primary way these STDs are spread is through any form of sexual intercourse, including vaginal, oral, or anal sex.

Human Papillomavirus
While chlamydia is the most commonly *reported* STD in the United States, health experts believe that genital **human papillomavirus (HPV)** infection is the most commonly *contracted* of all STDs. HPV is a virus that causes genital warts and warts on other parts of the body.

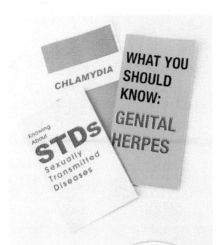

Many reliable sources of information about STDs exist for teens to access. In addition to medical professionals and pamphlets, what other sources could teens use to find accurate information?

Ken Karp/McGraw-Hill Education

Common Sexually Transmitted Diseases

Critical Thinking

Discussing Have students discuss why having an STD might affect the mental and emotional health of a teen. How might it interfere with their goals for the future? Embarrassment is one reason people do not seek treatment for STDs. Have students suggest ways to reduce embarrassment. OL

Active Learning

Guest Speaker Invite a health care professional to speak about STDs. Have each student prepare at least three questions to ask the speaker. OL

Reading Strategy

Emphasize Remind teens that, along with preventing STDs, abstinence is the only 100 percent effective way to prevent unplanned pregnancy. Practicing abstinence shows that teens take responsibility for their health. OL

Active Learning

Class Activity Ask students to think of strategies to make other teens aware of the benefits of abstinence for avoiding STDs. Ask them to consider what kind of campaigns might be effective in reaching teens. OL

Reading Strategy

Building Vocabulary Ask students to look at the vocabulary list and note any terms they have heard of before. Have them look these words up in the Glossary/Glosario to see how they are defined. Point out to students the reason the CDC has used the term "sexually transmitted infection" in place of "sexually transmitted disease" is because a person can be infected, or be infectious, without necessarily having the disease. Experts also feel that people may be more likely to seek testing and treatment for an infection. OL **EL**

Caption Answer: *Teens can find reliable and accurate health information on educational and government websites ending in .edu or .gov.*

Common Sexually Transmitted Diseases

Reading Strategy

Emphasize Certain types of human papillomaviruses cause warts or papillomas. While the symptoms are treatable, there is no cure and the warts can recur. In a minority of cases, the virus that causes them will always remain in the person's system. As you go over the STDs with the class, ask students to refer to the diagram of the male and female reproductive systems to see which parts of the reproductive system are affected by these diseases. OL

Critical Thinking

Research Have students research one of the STDs discussed in this lesson. When and where was the disease first reported, and when were treatments or cures discovered? AL

Caption Answer: *Genital warts*

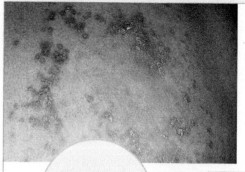

As is the case with many STDs, HPV infection often does not have symptoms. **What is the most common symptom of HPV?**

Q&A

What are a sexually active person's chances of contracting an STD?

Sexually active individuals are at high risk of contracting an STD. Three million teens contract an STD each year. One out of every four Americans will contract an STD at some point in their lifetime. About 75 percent of sexually active people have been infected with HPV.

More than 20 percent have genital herpes. In one single act of unprotected sex with an infected person, a female teen has a 30 percent chance of getting genital herpes and a 50 percent chance of getting gonorrhea.

Though many cases go unnoticed and unreported, it is believed that in 2018, about 13 million people contracted HPV in the United States. An estimated 42.5 million Americans already have the disease. HPV is most common in people in their late teens and early 20s. It is estimated that almost all sexually active individuals will acquire HPV infection at some point in their lives if they do not get the HPV vaccine.

Like many STDs, HPV infection often does not have symptoms. The most easily recognized symptom is **genital warts** (also called venereal warts), which are soft, moist, pink or red swellings that appear on the genitals and are caused by the human papillomavirus. Genital warts often grow in clusters and may spread into large masses. In females, the warts are found on the vulva, in the vagina, on the cervix, or around the anus. In males, genital warts are found on the penis, on the scrotum, or around the anus. Genital warts are found only rarely in the mouth or throat.

There are more than 100 types of HPV, most of which are harmless and cause benign conditions such as skin warts on other parts of the body. About 30 types of HPV are spread through oral, anal, or vaginal sexual contact. Certain types of genital HPV infection are linked to cervical cancer, including some that are also associated with cancers of the vulva, anus, and penis. A vaccine that can prevent HPV is now available. The vaccine prevents the types of HPV that can cause multiple types of cancer, including cervical cancer. The FDA recommends the vaccine for girls 11–12 years old. Females and males ages 9–26 can also benefit from the vaccine.

HPV is most commonly diagnosed through an examination of genital warts. Doctors sometimes use an acidic solution to make warts more visible. Genital warts may disappear by themselves, or they can be removed by laser or by being frozen, burned, or cut off. An antiviral drug can also be injected directly into larger warts, and other topical treatments may be used. Removal of the warts does not eliminate the virus, however—the warts can recur.

Chlamydia

Chlamydia is an STD that is caused by the bacterium Chlamydia trachomatis. The highest incidence of chlamydia in the United States is among teens and young adults. About two million Americans are currently infected; about four million became infected in 2018.

Despite the fact that it is easily cured, chlamydia often goes undiagnosed. Between 70 and 95 percent of women and 90 percent of men with the disease have no symptoms. During the early stages of infection, females can develop an abnormal vaginal discharge or a burning sensation when urinating. Males with symptoms may have a discharge from the penis and a burning sensation when urinating. If symptoms of early infection do occur, they usually appear within one to three weeks of sexual contact with an infected person.

Centers for Disease Control

Untreated infections may spread to other reproductive organs in both males and females, often without symptoms until permanent damage has occurred. A pregnant female can spread chlamydia to her baby during delivery, causing eye infection and sometimes pneumonia.

Diagnosis of chlamydia is made by collecting a specimen from the infected site and testing for bacteria. A more recent test involves checking a urine sample for bacteria. If chlamydia is diagnosed, antibiotics can easily cure the infection.

About 10 to 15 percent of females with untreated chlamydia will develop **pelvic inflammatory disease (PID).** This is a painful infection of the uterus, fallopian tubes, and/or ovaries. Permanent damage to uterus, fallopian tubes, and ovaries can result, along with severe pelvic pain, infertility, and an increased likelihood of ectopic pregnancy, or a pregnancy outside the womb. An active chlamydia infection also makes a female three to five times more likely to become infected with HIV if she is exposed to the virus.

Gonorrhea

Gonorrhea is an STD caused by bacteria that live in warm, moist areas of the body, such as mucous membranes. With more than one million new cases reported in the United States during 2018 alone, gonorrhea is an extremely common infectious disease. The bacterium *Neisseria gonorrhoeae* causes gonorrhea. In females, this organism can thrive in mucous membranes of the cervix, uterus, and fallopian tubes, and in the urethra, mouth, throat, and anus of both females and males.

Teens and young adults have the highest incidence of gonorrhea. The rate of reported infections has been higher among men than women since 2013. The rate of gonorrhea among men increased about 61% during 2018 and 2019. The rate among women increased about 44% during the same time period. Most males do show some symptoms of the disease when they are infected. These usually appear two to ten days after infection. Symptoms of genital infection include:

- A burning sensation when urinating
- A white, yellow, or green discharge from the penis
- Painful or swollen testicles

In females, the disease may go unnoticed because females often show no symptoms. Early symptoms in females may be so mild that they are often mistaken for another type of infection. Symptomatic females have a burning sensation when urinating and a yellow vaginal discharge that is sometimes tinged with blood. In a rectal infection, symptoms in both males and females may include:

- Anal discharge
- Painful rectal itch
- Soreness
- Bleeding
- Painful bowel movements

A gonorrhea infection of the throat causes few symptoms.

Common Sexually Transmitted Diseases **101**

More About...

> ### More About...
>
> **Gonorrhea Prevention** Most states require routine administration of antibiotic eye drops to newborn babies to prevent blindness caused by gonorrhea.

LESSON 1
Common Sexually Transmitted Diseases

Critical Thinking

Protecting a Newborn Ask students why they think cesarean delivery protects a baby from HSV-2. OL

LESSON 1

Common Sexually Transmitted Diseases

Critical Thinking

Discussing Have students discuss the importance of sexually active people being tested for STDs even if they are symptom free. Tell them to consider some of the consequences of living with an STD. OL

Caption Answer: *Gonorrhea can be treated with antibiotics. Left untreated, it can cause epididymitis and sterility in males, PID in females, and it can become life threatening.*

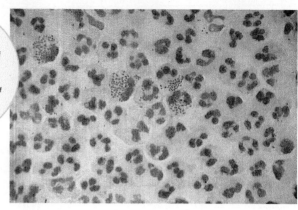

Gonorrhea is an STD caused by bacteria that live in warm, moist areas of the body, such as mucous membranes. **What is the treatment for gonorrhea? Explain what can happen if someone who is infected does not get treatment.**

Untreated gonorrhea in females can lead to PID. In males, gonorrhea can cause epididymitis, an inflammation of the testicles that can cause sterility. Gonorrhea can also affect the prostate gland and cause scarring inside the urethra. In both sexes, gonorrhea can spread to the blood or joints, at which point the disease becomes life threatening.

Gonorrhea is treated with antibiotics. Chlamydia infection is often also present in people with gonorrhea, so antibiotics to treat both conditions are usually given at the same time. People with gonorrhea are more likely to contract HIV if exposed; those with both HIV infection and gonorrhea are also more likely to spread HIV.

Genital Herpes

Genital herpes is an STD caused by the herpes simplex virus. Herpes simplex 1 usually causes cold sores in or near the mouth. According to the CDC, an estimated 18.6 million people in the United States currently have genital herpes. About 570,000 new cases were reported in 2018.

A person infected with genital herpes frequently has no symptoms. If symptoms do occur, it is usually within two to five days of exposure. However, it may take up to 30 days for symptoms to appear. Symptoms consist of an outbreak of blisters on or around the genitals or rectum. Some people may also have a fever and swollen glands. After the blisters break, painful lesions remain that take two to four weeks to heal. Within a few weeks or months, another outbreak may occur, but it is usually less severe than the first. A person may have four or five such episodes in the first year but fewer as the years go by.

The virus is spread from open sores during sexual contact, but is also can be transmitted when lesions are not present. Once a person has been infected with herpes simplex virus type 2 (HSV-2), he or she will always have the disease and can spread it to other people. This is one reason why so many people have the disease.

Certain antiviral medications can reduce the duration and severity of episodes, but the virus itself remains in the person's system forever. Consistent and correct use of condoms can help protect against infections. However, condoms may not completely cover the sores and the virus can still spread.

HSV-2 can be fatal to newborns if contracted from the mother during delivery. Pregnant females who have an active genital herpes infection usually have a cesarean delivery to protect the baby.

Herpes simplex virus type 1 (HSV-1) is also common in the United States but is not considered an STD. HSV-1 causes cold sores, which are blisters on the mouth and lips of infected people. The virus can be spread by saliva to another person, or through kissing and touching when lesions are present.

An HSV-1 infection can occur on the genitals following oral-genital contact with a person who has a cold sore. Oral-genital contact with a person who has HSV-2 can also cause HSV-2 infection on the mouth. Anyone who is having an active episode of HSV-1 or HSV-2 should avoid touching the lesions. Careful personal hygiene, including hand washing, helps prevent the spread of the herpes virus to other people and other areas of one's own body.

Remember that abstinence is the only 100 percent effective method to avoid contracting STDs. You can protect yourself from the risks of STDs by practicing abstinence from sexual activity before marriage and by using refusal skills to avoid situations in which you may be at risk. Choosing friends who support your decision to remain abstinent will help you in your commitment.

Character Check

Saying no to sexual activity is an important way to take responsibility for your health. You can make a list of reasons to practice abstinence. For example, "I value my health." Think about how these can be used as part of your refusal strategies if you are pressured to engage in sexual activity.

Lesson 1 Review

Facts and Vocabulary

1. Define *sexually transmitted diseases*. Explain why they are difficult to track.

2. Describe the relationship between high-risk behaviors and the risk for contracting STDs.

3. What is human papillomavirus and how common is it?

4. Name three things you can do to reduce your risk of contracting an STD.

5. Name some of the results of untreated gonorrhea.

Thinking Critically

6. **Synthesize.** You and a friend have agreed to help each other remain abstinent. Your friend has just told you that she has accepted a date with a boy who has a reputation for being sexually active. What would you tell your friend about developing strategies to prevent the spread of STDs?

7. **Compare.** How are the early symptoms of chlamydia and gonorrhea similar?

Applying Health Skills

8. **Practicing Healthful Behaviors.** Communicate the importance of practicing abstinence from sexual activity. Create an outline for a pamphlet with guidelines teens can follow to avoid risky situations and behaviors that may compromise their decision to practice abstinence.

Common Sexually Transmitted Diseases **103**

ASSESS

Reteaching Have students make a chart listing the types of STDs they learned about in this lesson, and the symptoms, diagnoses, and treatments of each.

Enrichment Ask students to find current articles regarding the spread of STDs, especially among teens. Have them share what they learn with the class.

Sum up this lesson by asking students to state one fact that they have learned about STDs and their consequences.

Lesson 1 Review Answers

1. Sexually transmitted diseases spread from person to person through sexual contact. They are difficult to track because some people who have them may not exhibit symptoms.

2. Answers may vary but should include: engaging in sexual activity without using any barrier protection method; using alcohol and other drugs.

3. It is the virus that causes genital warts and can cause cancer in both males and females. Health experts believe that genital HPV infection is the most common STD.

4. Practicing abstinence from sexual activity; using refusal skills; choosing friends who support abstinence.

5. Some of the results are: PID; epididymitis; effect on the prostate; scarring inside the urethra; damage to the blood or joints, at which point the disease becomes life threatening.

6. Answers will vary.

7. The early symptoms for females often go unnoticed but may involve a burning sensation when urinating and an abnormal vaginal discharge; the early symptoms for males may involve a burning sensation when urinating and a discharge from the penis.

8. Pamphlets will vary.

Other Sexually Transmitted Diseases

FOCUS

BIG IDEA Sexually transmitted diseases pose serious health risks.

Explain to students that in this lesson they will learn more about other STDs and their treatments.

Reading Strategy

Problems and Solutions Students' summaries and lists will vary.

QUICKWRITE

Write the following on the board for students to answer: *How might a person contract an STD without being sexually active?* **Students may mention sharing needles from injected drug use or body piercing, transmission from mother to baby during pregnancy or childbirth, or contact with infested bed linens or clothing.**

Student Objectives

- Develop and analyze strategies to prevent spreading STDs.
- Identify, describe, and assess community health services available for prevention and treatment of STDs.
- Analyze the importance of abstinence in the prevention of STDs.

TEACH

Writing Support

Research Tell students that there are several different types of hepatitis (A, B, C, D, and E), not all of which are sexually transmitted. Ask students to research one of the hepatitis types and write a few paragraphs summarizing their results. Have students share what they learn about its causes, symptoms, and treatments with the class. AL

Other Sexually Transmitted Diseases

BIG IDEA Sexually transmitted diseases pose serious health risks.

BEFORE YOU READ

Problems and Solutions. Write a brief summary describing some of the behaviors that you think can expose someone to an STD. Add a list of tips to prevent the transmission of these STDs.

Vocabulary
hepatitis B (HBV)
syphilis
vaginitis
trichomoniasis
bacterial vaginosis (BV)
pubic lice
scabies

QUICK WRITE

List two or more effects of STDs. Write two refusal skills you can use to avoid contracting an STD.

Hepatitis B

Hepatitis B (HBV) is a viral STD that attacks the liver and can cause extreme illness and death. HBV is transmitted when blood or other body fluids from an infected person enter the body of a person who is not immune to the disease. The virus can be spread through sexual activity or the use of unclean needles. Sharing needles for drug use or having body piercings and tattoos are high-risk behaviors. An infected mother can also pass the virus to her baby during delivery.

It is estimated that more than 100,000 people in the United States currently have the acute form of the disease. The acute form can develop into a chronic disease that may lead to serious health conditions or death. An estimated 1.6 million people in the United States now have a chronic HBV infection, and about 1,600 HBV-related deaths were reported in 2018.

Among adults, about 50 percent with HBV have no symptoms. When symptoms do occur, they include:

- Jaundice
- Fatigue
- Abdominal pain
- Nausea
- Vomiting
- Joint pain
- Loss of appetite

People infected with HBV can be treated with drugs. However, these are effective in only about 40 percent of individuals. Approximately 15 to 25 percent of people with chronic HBV infections die of related liver disease.

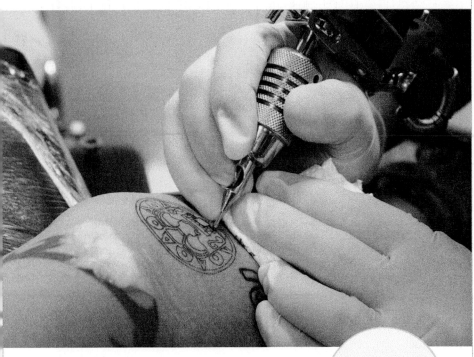

A vaccine against HBV has been available since 1982 and is routinely given to children from birth to age 18. Health care and public safety workers, and anyone else exposed to blood or other body fluids, should also be vaccinated against HBV.

Hepatitis B (HBV) can be spread through needles used for body piercing or tattoos. **What are some other high-risk behaviors that teens should avoid in order to keep from getting HBV?**

Hepatitis C

According to the CDC, approximately 2.4 million Americans have chronic infection from the hepatitis C virus. This disease can lead to chronic liver disease, liver cancer, and liver failure.

Chronic hepatitis is often asymptomatic, or presents no symptoms, and the disease progresses slowly. Infected individuals may not even realize they have the disease until damage is detected during a routine physical examination.

Hepatitis C is transmitted through sexual contact and other direct contact with contaminated blood, such as shared or dirty needles used in injected drugs. A therapy combining specific medications can reduce the effects of hepatitis C, but there is no 100 percent cure.

Other Sexually Transmitted Diseases

Active Learning

Class Activity Have students write about the serious risk of STDs to teens. The information should be presented in article form, such as for a teen magazine. OL

Reading Strategy

Building Vocabulary Tell students that the root *hepat-* comes from the Greek word for "liver" and that the root *–itis* comes from the Latin word for "inflammation." Ask students what they think the word *hepatitis* means. Then ask them what they think *vaginitis* means. Have them check their answers in the Glossary/Glosario. AL

Caption Answer: *Sexual activity and sharing needles for drug use.*

Other Sexually Transmitted Diseases

Critical Thinking

Medical Treatment Have students evaluate the following situation: A person with a small sore on his or her genitals puts some medicated cream on the sore and it goes away. The person says he or she does not need to see a doctor about it because it has gone away. OL

Reading Strategy

Emphasize Stress to students that although there are non-prescription treatments for some types of vaginitis, it is important to see a doctor to ensure a correct diagnosis. OL

In the United States today, three doses of hepatitis B vaccine are routinely administered to infants. Children and adolescents who were not immunized as infants receive the vaccine during later visits to their pediatrician.

Health Minute

The Consequences of STDs
Be aware of the problems STDs can cause:

- Some STDs are incurable, and medical treatment can't eliminate them from the body.
- Some STDs can cause cancer.
- Some STDs can be passed from an infected female to her child before, during, or after birth.

Syphilis

Syphilis is an STD caused by the bacterium Treponema pallidum; it progresses in stages. It is spread by direct contact with a chancre, a painless sore that appears early in the disease. However, it can also be spread by contract with the infectious rash that appears later. The disease is transmitted primarily through sexual activity, including vaginal, oral, and anal sex.

Pregnant females who have untreated syphilis can pass the disease to the fetus during pregnancy, which can cause stillbirth or the death of the infant shortly after birth. Infected infants who receive no treatment may have developmental delays, have seizures, or die from the disease.

Untreated syphilis progresses through three stages:

- **Primary Stage.** Within 10 to 90 days of infection, a small, firm, round sore called a chancre appears at the spot where the bacterium entered the body. The sore is painless and lasts for three to six weeks, after which it disappears, even without treatment.

- **Secondary Stage.** An infectious rash of rough, red or reddish-brown spots appears on the palms of the hands and the soles of the feet. Flu-like symptoms, hair loss, and weight loss can also appear. This rash also disappears without treatment.

- **Late Syphilis.** During a latent period usually lasting several years, external signs of the disease disappear. The organism remains in the body, however, damaging organs such as the brain, nerves, eyes, heart, blood vessels, liver, bones, and joints. Symptoms of late syphilis include slow, progressive loss of muscle coordination, paralysis, blindness, and dementia. If damage to tissues is severe enough, death follows.

Syphilis is diagnosed by a blood test or by laboratory examination of material from the primary chancre or secondary-stage rash. The disease is easily cured with antibiotics, but once damage to internal organs has occurred, there is no way to repair it. People who are infected with syphilis are also more likely to contract and transmit HIV through sexual contact.

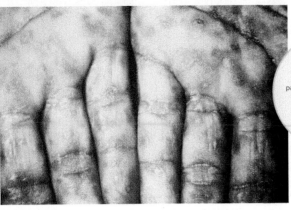

The infectious rash of secondary-stage syphilis appears on the palms of the hands and the soles of the feet. **What happens when these external signs disappear?**

Trichomoniasis and Bacterial Vaginosis

There are many types of **vaginitis**, an inflammation of the vagina caused by various organisms. **Trichomoniasis** is a type of vaginitis caused by the parasite *Trichomonas vaginalis*. It affects both females and males.

Infected males experience the following symptoms:

- Irritation inside the penis
- Mild discharge
- Slight burning after urinating or ejaculating

Infected females experience the following symptoms:

- Foamy, yellow-green vaginal discharge that has a strong odor
- Genital irritation
- Genital itching
- Discomfort during intercourse and urination

Bacterial vaginosis (BV) affects only females. It is a type of vaginitis caused by an imbalance of bacteria normally found in the vagina. Little is known about the cause, but having sexual intercourse with a new partner and douching may be contributing factors. Symptoms of BV include white or gray vaginal discharge with a strong odor, as well as itching and burning around the vagina. However, BV may be asymptomatic, meaning it doesn't present any symptoms. BV increases the risk of developing gonorrhea and PID, endangering the uterus and fallopian tubes. Both trichomoniasis and BV can make HIV infection more likely.

Did You Know?

Using a latex condom can provide protection from the spread of certain STDs, including bacterial vaginosis, gonorrhea, chlamydia, syphilis, and HIV. However, it does not protect against all STDs. For example, HSV-2, HPV, pubic lice, and scabies are easily transmitted through contact with an infected area not covered by a condom.

CDC

Other Sexually Transmitted Diseases

Active Learning

Explain Using a latex condom can provide protection from the spread of certain STDs, including bacterial vaginosis, gonorrhea, chlamydia, syphilis, and HIV. However, it does not protect against all STDs. For example, HSV-2, HPV, pubic lice, and scabies are easily transmitted through contact with an infected area not covered by a condom. OL

Health Skills Practice

Communication Ask students how one might overcome the embarrassment of telling a partner that he or she has an STD. OL

Critical Thinking

Transmission Remind students that pubic lice and scabies can be transferred from person to person through clothing and bed linens. Ask students what actions someone being treated for pubic lice or scabies might take to ensure the cleanliness of their clothing and linens. OL

Caption Answer: *The organism remains in the body and begins to damage organs. If tissue damage is severe, death occurs.*

Other Sexually Transmitted Diseases

Critical Thinking

Discussing Tell students that STDs are often referred to as "silent epidemics" or "silent killers." Ask them to discuss why such labels are applied to STDs. Ask students to make a list of what they might say to a friend who is reluctant to see a doctor about a possible STD. OL

Reading Strategy

Research Ask students to research how sexually transmitted diseases are tracked and by whom. Ask them to consider why it is helpful to track a disease. AL

Caption Answer: *The main symptom is intense itching. Special medicated shampoos can be used to kill pubic lice.*

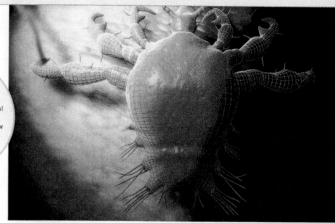

Pubic lice are tiny parasitic insects that infest the genital area. **What is the main symptom of pubic lice? How can they be treated?**

Pubic Lice

Pubic lice are tiny parasitic insects, also known as crabs, that infest the genital area of humans. Pubic lice are usually spread through sexual contact. In rare circumstances, they can spread through infested bed linens, towels, and clothing, since the lice can survive for a short time without a host.

The main symptom of lice is intense itching. The lice usually live in pubic hair but can also live in the coarse hair of legs, armpits, mustaches, beards, eyebrows, and eyelashes. Lice that infest the hair on a person's head are not pubic lice.

Special medicated shampoos that kill pubic lice are available both over the counter and with a doctor's prescription. These shampoos are harsh and should not be used on the eyebrows or eyelashes. For those areas, a special ointment that will not damage the eyes is available by prescription. Bed linens, towels, and clothing must also be treated to prevent re-infection.

Scabies

Scabies is an infestation of the skin with microscopic mites called Sarcoptes scabiei. It is spread by sharing infested bedding and clothing and through prolonged skin-to-skin contact. Scabies cannot be transmitted by shaking someone's hand.

Symptoms of scabies appear four to six weeks after contact and include a pimple-like rash in the following areas of the body:

- Between the fingers
- In skin folds on the body
- Penis
- Breasts
- Shoulder blades

The rash causes severe itching, and sores can become infected from scratching. Fewer than ten mites are usually present on an infested person, so diagnosis of scabies can be difficult. Examining the burrows made by the mites provides the best means of diagnosis. All members of affected households, along with all sexual partners of infested people, should be treated at the same time as the infected person by using special lotions that kill the mites.

Being Responsible About STDs

STDs can be prevented, and it is every individual's responsibility to practice behaviors that prevent the spread of STDs. Obtaining treatment for STDs is also an important responsibility. STDs will not go away if a person waits long enough; treatment must be sought from a doctor or a public health clinic. For treatment to be successful, a person must do the following:

- Get tested regularly if the person is engaged in regular sexual activity.
- Seek treatment immediately if the person discovers they have an STD, or thinks he or she might have an STD after sexual contact with a partner.
- Follow the doctor's orders for treatment and take all the medication prescribed. Do not stop taking the medication even if the symptoms have gone away.
- Notify everyone with whom the person has had any sexual contact.
- Avoid sharing needles or needles used in tattooing or piercings.
- Remember that abstinence is the only 100% effective method of preventing re-infection or transmission of STDs.

Health Minute

Knowing the Facts Can Help You Make Responsible Decisions Facts about STDs:

- The body does not build up immunity to STDs, so re-infection can occur.
- Symptoms of some STDs may go away without treatment, but the disease remains in the body.
- It is possible to have an STD without knowing it.

Lesson 2 Review

Facts and Vocabulary

1. What is hepatitis B and how is it transmitted?

2. How is syphilis spread?

3. What occurs during each phase of syphilis?

4. What is the main symptom of pubic lice?

5. What is scabies?

Thinking Critically

6. **Synthesize.** Analyze strategies to prevent the spread of syphilis.

7. **Analyze.** Describe the importance and benefits of abstinence. How can teens ensure that they do not contract an STD?

Applying Health Skills

8. **Communication Skills.** Identify, describe, and assess community health services available for the prevention and treatment of STDs. Suppose that a friend came to you and told you that he had a painless sore on the genitals that disappeared within two weeks. What would you advise him to do first? What other advice would you give him?

Other Sexually Transmitted Diseases **109**

Other Sexually Transmitted Diseases

ASSESS

Reteaching Have students add to the chart they created for the last lesson *hepatitis B, hepatitis C, syphilis, trichomoniasis, bacterial vaginosis, pubic lice,* and *scabies,* including the symptoms, diagnoses, and treatments of each.

Enrichment Tell students that in some states, a couple is required to have their blood tested for STDs and other conditions before a marriage license can be issued. Ask students why some states require such tests.

Sum up the lesson by asking students to list the three most important things they learned in this lesson about avoiding STDs.

Lesson 2 Review Answers

1. Hepatitis B is a viral infection that attacks the liver. It is transmitted when blood or other body fluids from an infected person enter the body of a person who is not immune.

2. Syphilis is spread by direct contact or through sexual activity, but pregnant females can pass the disease to the fetus during pregnancy.

3. Primary stage: a small, firm, round sore called a chancre appears at the spot where it entered the body. Secondary stage: An infectious rash appears on the palms of the hands and the soles of the feet. Late stage: external signs of the disease disappear, but it remains in the body damaging the organs.

4. Intense itching is the main symptom.

5. Scabies is an infestation of the skin with microscopic mites.

6. Get tested, seek treatment, notify everyone with whom you have had sexual contact, or use abstinence.

7. They can make the decision to practice abstinence.

8. Answers will vary, but students should advise the friend to see a doctor.

MODULE 7
Assessment Answers

1. C. Some STDs have no symptoms in some people, others don't produce symptoms for a long time, and still others have symptoms that go away while the STD remains in the body and can be spread.

2. Abstinence. Abstaining from high-risk behaviors, such as alcohol or drug use and sexual activity before marriage, is the only method that is 100 percent effective in avoiding STDs.

3. Often, there are no symptoms until permanent damage has occurred.

4. It is a painful infection of the uterus, fallopian tubes, and/or ovaries. Permanent damage to these structures, with severe pelvic pain, infertility, and increased likelihood of ectopic pregnancy, can result.

5. It is most commonly diagnosed by examining genital warts. It is treated by having the genital warts removed by laser or by being frozen, burned, or cut off; or by having an antiviral drug injected into larger warts and/or using other topical treatments. Removal of the warts does not eliminate the virus, however, and the warts often recur.

6. One reason is that once a person has been infected, he or she will always have the disease and can spread it to other people.

7. An infectious rash of non-itchy, rough, red or reddish-brown spots appears on the palms of the hands and the soles of the feet. Flulike symptoms, hair loss, and weight loss can also be present. The rash disappears without treatment.

8. Syphilis is diagnosed by a blood test or by a laboratory examination of material from the primary chancre or the secondary stage rash.

9. Pubic lice are treated with a special medicated over-the-counter or prescription shampoo.

10. Follow the doctor's orders for treatment and take all the medication prescribed; Notify everyone with whom the infected person has had any sexual contact; Remember that abstinence is the only effective method of preventing reinfection or transmission of STDs.

11. STDs can be prevented by making healthy choices and not engaging in sexual activity. There is no effective way to protect against the common cold.

12. Answers will vary, but students might discuss a patient's need for privacy in order to seek treatment and parents' concern for the health of a teen who may have an STD or is engaging in risky behaviors.

13. The partners could become infected, as could a baby, if the infected person is female and becomes pregnant. Partners could also infect other people, thus spreading the disease.

14. STDs affect the health of infected individuals and the health of others.

15. Radio announcements will vary.

16. Answers will vary, but students may suggest that teens are not as well informed as adults, that they may engage in risky behaviors, or that they believe they are immune from harm because of their age.

Reviewing Facts and Vocabulary

1. Which of the following statements is true?
   a. A person can always tell if a sexual partner has an STD.
   b. A person cannot get an STD if he or she has only one sexual partner.
   c. A person could have an STD and not know it.

2. What is the most effective way to avoid getting an STD?

3. Why does chlamydia often go undiagnosed?

4. What is pelvic inflammatory disease? What can result from this STD?

5. How is HPV diagnosed and treated?

6. Why do so many people have HSV-2?

7. Describe the secondary stage of syphilis.

8. How would a doctor determine whether a person has syphilis?

9. Explain how pubic lice are treated.

10. What steps should be taken to treat and prevent the spread of STDs?

Writing Critically

11. Synthesize. Write a brief summary describing how STDs are different from most other communicable diseases, such as the common cold, in terms of prevention.

12. Analyze. Write a paragraph on whether you think doctors should be required to inform the parents of a patient under the age of 18 who has an STD. Explain your reasons.

13. Synthesize. Write a summary describing what might be the consequences if a person infected with an STD never told his sexual partners that he has an STD.

14. Analyze. Write a summary explaining why prevention and treatment of STDs is the responsibility of every individual.

Applying Health Skills

15. Advocacy. Analyze the importance of abstinence in the prevention of STDs. Write a 30-second radio announcement promoting prevention of STDs in your community.

16. Analyzing Influences. Write an essay in which you explain why you think STDs are such a serious problem in the adolescent age group.

BEYOND THE CLASSROOM ACTIVITIES

PARENT INVOLVEMENT
Discussing. Discuss with your parents or guardians the issues of STDs, medical information, and privacy for minors under the age of 18. Discuss whether adolescents, adults, or people of any age should be required to inform others if they have an STD.

SCHOOL AND COMMUNITY
Report to the Class. Do research at the library or on the Internet to find further information on a particular STD. Write a report to share with the class. Include symptoms, diagnosis, treatment, and dangers that can occur when the STD is not treated. Include a visual aid when presenting the report to the class.

BEYOND THE CLASSROOM

Parent Involvement: Discussing. Have students discuss with their parents or guardians the issues of STDs, medical information, and privacy for minors under the age of 18. Suggest that they also talk about whether adolescents, adults, or people of any age should be required to inform others if they have an STD.

School and Community: Report to the Class. Have students do research at the library or on the Internet to find further information on a particular STD. Direct them to write a report to share with the class. Reports should include symptoms, diagnosis, treatment, and dangers that can occur when the STD is not treated. Students should include a visual aid when presenting their reports to the class.

- Encourage students to participate in activities that involve parents and the community.

- Encourage students to discuss these issues with parents or guardians.

- Reports will vary depending on the STD students choose to research.

MODULE 8 | HIV and AIDS

MODULE 8	STANDARDS / NOTES ✎	LESSON ASSESSMENT
	Use this space for standards and notes.	Module 8 Assessment Online assessment
LESSON 1 **What Is HIV/AIDS** **BIG IDEA.** HIV/AIDs is a deadly disease that destroys the body's immune system.		Lesson 1 Review Online assessment
LESSON 2 **HIV/AIDS Testing and Treatment** **BIG IDEA.** There are many options available today for diagnosing the presence of HIV/AIDS and receiving support.		Lesson 2 Review Online assessment

(30 MIN. — Lesson 1)
(30 MIN. — Lesson 2)

Key to Abilities   Teaching Strategies and Activities have been coded for ability level and appropriateness.

AL Activities for students working above grade level

BL Activities for students working below grade level

OL Activities for students working on grade level

EL Activities for English Learners

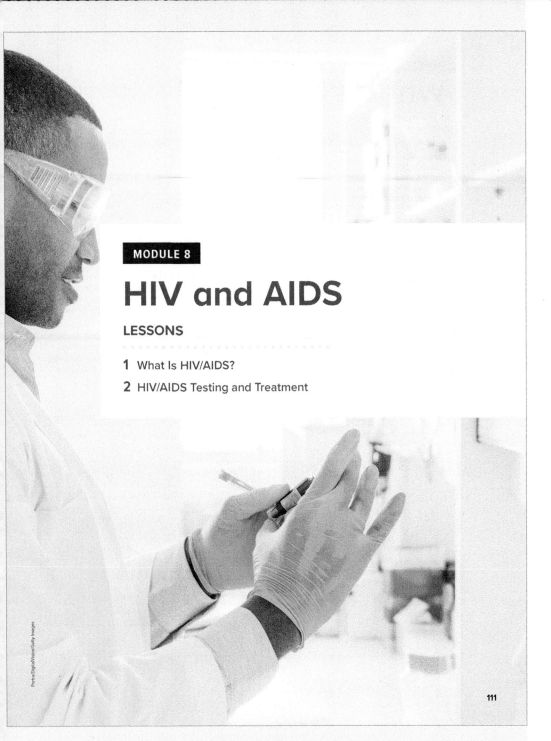

MODULE 8
HIV and AIDS

LESSONS

1 What Is HIV/AIDS?
2 HIV/AIDS Testing and Treatment

111

HIV and AIDS

Module Overview Module 8 focuses on the stages and symptoms of HIV and AIDS and discusses methods of transmission and sources of medical and community support.

LESSON 1
Identify the stages and symptoms of HIV and AIDS and explain the way HIV is and is not transmitted.

LESSON 2
Identify the tests, symptoms, and medications associated with HIV and AIDS and identify HIV/AIDS support services available in the community.

Activating Prior Knowledge

Using Visuals Researchers are working to improve diagnostic methods to identify HIV so that early treatment is possible. Have students list the ways that they know HIV can be transmitted.

Student Objectives:

- Identify the stages and symptoms of HIV and AIDS and explain the way HIV is and is not transmitted.
- Identify the tests, symptoms, and medications associated with HIV and AIDS and identify HIV/AIDS support services available in the community.

What Is HIV/AIDS?

FOCUS

BIG IDEA HIV/AIDs is a deadly disease that destroys the body's immune system.

Tell students that in this lesson they will learn the ways HIV can be spread . They will also learn about ways HIV is not spread.

Reading Strategy

Predict Students' questions will vary.

QUICKWRITE

Before students answer, write the following on the board for students to answer: *How is HIV spread? How is HIV not spread?* **Accept reasonable responses.**

Student Objectives:

- Identify the stages and symptoms of HIV and AIDS.
- Explain the relationship between risky behaviors and the transmission of HIV.
- Explain why abstinence is the only method that is 100 percent effective in preventing HIV infection.

TEACH

Reading Strategy

Discussing Emphasize that AIDS is caused by a virus called HIV. Have students identify other diseases caused by a virus, such as polio, chicken pox, measles, herpes, influenza, mononucleosis, mumps, rabies, and the common cold. Point out that many of these diseases can be prevented through immunizations. Tell students that isolating HIV was the first step in the ongoing process of finding a way to stop AIDS. OL

Caption Answer: *Once inside the cell, the body cannot fight it, and the virus begins to make copies of itself.*

What Is HIV/AIDS?

BEFORE YOU READ

Predict. Scan the headings, subheadings, and photo captions. Write down a list of questions you have about HIV and AIDS. After reading the lesson, review your list and fill in the answers.

Vocabulary

human immunodeficiency virus (HIV)
acquired immune deficiency syndrome (AIDS)
lymphocytes
antibodies
AIDS-opportunistic illnesses (AIDS-OIs)

BIG IDEA HIV/AIDs is a disease that destroys the body's immune system.

QUICK WRITE

Write a letter to a friend who was sexually active in the past but has been abstinent for more than a year. The friend is now considering being tested for HIV. How would you advise your friend?

What are HIV and AIDS?

Human immunodeficiency virus (HIV) is a virus that attacks the immune system. Once HIV enters the body, the virus destroys disease-fighting cells. When these cells are attacked, the body loses the ability to fight illness. **Acquired immune deficiency syndrome (AIDS)** can result from HIV and is a potentially fatal disease in which the immune system is weakened. AIDS is the final stage of infection caused by HIV.

AIDS is a global crisis, with no known cure. In 2020, 1.5 million people were infected with HIV, and 660,000 died of AIDS. According to the World Health Organization (WHO), more than 37.7 million people are currently living with HIV. Most individuals with HIV can still live long lives due to medical advancements in HIV treatment.

Once inside the cell, HIV is safe from attack by the immune system's antibodies. **How does this make HIV particularly dangerous?**

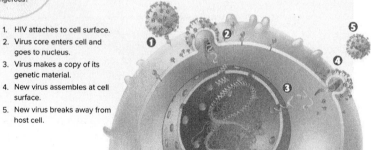

1. HIV attaches to cell surface.
2. Virus core enters cell and goes to nucleus.
3. Virus makes a copy of its genetic material.
4. New virus assembles at cell surface.
5. New virus breaks away from host cell.

How Does HIV Affect the Body?

The body contains specialized white blood cells to help fight pathogens, or disease-causing organisms. Known as **lymphocytes,** these cells provide the body with immunity. One type of lymphocyte stimulates the body to produce **antibodies.**

As HIV enters and destroys these lymphocyte cells, the virus reproduces itself. As more cells are infected, more are destroyed. The immune system becomes weakened and is eventually destroyed. The body is then extremely weakened and vulnerable to infections. These are called **AIDS-opportunistic illnesses (AIDS-OIs).**

It takes between three and six weeks after a person is infected to detect the HIV antibodies in their system. Once detected, HIV typically goes through four specific stages:

- **Asymptomatic stage.** This stage can last ten years or longer. The virus is largely confined to the lymph nodes, where it invades and takes over or destroys specific lymphocytes, known as helper T cells. There are no outward signs of infection.

- **Middle stage.** Also called the acute antiretroviral stage, this stage occurs in about 40 to 70 percent of infected patients. Patients experience fever, headache, sore throat, rash, diarrhea, and enlarged lymph nodes.

- **Symptomatic stage.** The helper T cell count falls to 200–400 per milliliter of blood. This low level contains too few lymphocytes to help the body ward off the disease. The infected person experiences flu-like symptoms such as headache, fever, body aches, swollen glands, diminished appetite, unexplained weight loss, and skin rashes.

- **AIDS stage.** The helper T cells are scarce at this stage, allowing AIDS-OIs to enter the body. AIDS-OIs would not be able to exist if the immune system were healthy. These illnesses cause the suffering and death associated with AIDS.

A person can be infected with HIV for as long as ten years before it progresses into AIDS. Researchers are investigating the reasons why a small number of people infected ten or more years ago show no AIDS symptoms.

Researchers are working to improve diagnostic methods to identify HIV so that early treatment is possible. **List the ways you know of in which HIV can be transmitted.**

Kris Timken/Blend Images LLC

What Is HIV/AIDS?

Active Learning

Class Activity Ask students to list five safe, entertaining activities they have participated in over the last week that offered no risk of contracting HIV. Have volunteers read activities from their lists and write these on the board under the heading "No-Risk Behaviors." You might also want to use this heading for a bulletin board that students can decorate with pictures cut out from magazines or newspapers. OL

Writing Support

Research Have students research more about the origins of HIV. Have them write a few paragraphs explaining their results. Have them share their findings with the class. AL

Cultural Awareness

Emphasize Remind teens that you cannot determine whether a person has HIV based on appearance. OL

Critical Thinking

Discussing Have students explain, using their own words, the meaning of the term *AIDS-opportunistic illness.* **Answer: an illness that would not harm a person with a healthy immune system; an illness that takes advantage of the weaknesses in the immune system caused by HIV.** Have them explain the statement, "A person does not die from AIDS but from another disease or opportunistic illness." **HIV destroys the immune system but the virus itself does not cause death. The damage to the immune system leaves the body with no way to fight off AIDS-opportunistic illnesses, which then prove fatal.** OL

Caption Answer: *Answers will vary, but may include blood transfusions before, during, and after birth; sexual contact; use of contaminated needles.*

What Is HIV/AIDS?

Critical Thinking

Discussing Review each of the ways HIV is spread. Have students discuss how HIV can enter the blood. Have students reread the section "How HIV is Transmitted." Then add that cuts in the skin of the penis and on the vaginal wall can be so tiny that they do not bleed visibly. Therefore, most people are unaware of them. Ask students why these cuts are dangerous. OL

Debate Have students debate the following statement: "An individual infected with HIV should be allowed to play contact sports." Encourage students to support their positions with factual information from the lesson about HIV transmission and how it might impact such a situation. OL

Reading Strategy

Building Vocabulary Tell students that the word *syndrome* comes from the Greek words *syn-,* meaning "with" or "together with," and *dramein,* meaning "to run." Ask students to explain why they think AIDS is a syndrome. AL

Did You Know?

The Ryan White Comprehensive AIDS Resources Emergency (CARE) Act was passed in 1990. It was named for the boy who was infected with HIV at age 13 and died at 18. This act approved funds for AIDS testing, counseling, and treatment for cities and states hardest hit by the disease. Ryan White was one of the first national spokespersons for people with AIDS. Celebrities, musicians, sports personalities, and others continue efforts to raise awareness of the HIV/AIDS issue and advocate for funding and research.

How HIV is Transmitted

HIV is carried in body fluids such as blood, semen, vaginal secretions, and breast milk. A person may contract the virus if the infection is present in these body fluids. These infected fluids can access the body through breaks in the skin such as cuts, sores, or through tiny breaks in the capillaries of mucous membranes. Mucous membranes can be found in the mouth, eyes, nose, vagina, rectum, and the opening of the penis. Use of contaminated needles and injected drugs also put a person at risk.

Behaviors Known to Transmit HIV

Certain activities are far more likely than others to transmit HIV. Nearly 100 percent of new HIV infections in the United States are contracted in one of two ways: sexual activity and injection drug use. Sexual activity with an infected partner accounts for about 75 percent of HIV infections. Injection drug use accounts for close to 25 percent of new HIV infections.

- **Sexual contact.** Unprotected sexual activity with an infected partner is the main way that HIV is spread. During sexual contact, the virus usually enters the body through tiny tears in fragile tissue or breaks in capillaries of mucous membranes. Such tears and breaks are common during genital-genital and anal-genital contact. The larger the number of sex partners a person has, the greater the risk of coming in contact with HIV. People with other sexually transmitted diseases (STDs) are more likely to contract HIV and spread the virus.

- **Use of contaminated needles.** When a drug user injects drugs into their veins with a needle, blood remains on and within the needle after use. If the person is infected with HIV, anyone else who uses the same needle can contract HIV. Sharing any kind of needle—to inject drugs, make tattoos, or create body piercings—puts a person at risk for HIV contact.

Recent studies have found that in addition to needle sharing, people who abuse drugs that are injected are more likely to engage in high-risk behaviors such as having unprotected sexual activity of any kind. Any person may be infected with HIV regardless of age, race, or sexual orientation if they participate in unprotected sexual activity.

Situations Known to Transmit HIV

HIV can be transmitted whenever blood from an infected person is handled if proper precautions are not followed. These situations include:

- **Before, during, or after birth.** A pregnant female infected with HIV can pass the virus to her unborn baby through the placenta. During birth, HIV can enter the baby's body through tiny cuts in the skin. After birth, a breast-fed baby can contract HIV from the mother's milk. Special drugs given to the mother during pregnancy can greatly reduce the baby's risk of contracting HIV. Drug treatment and delivery by cesarean section lowers this risk to about 5 percent.

- **Blood transfusions.** People who donate blood are *not* at risk for contracting HIV, because blood donation centers discard needles after each use. Since March 1985, all donated blood in the United States has been tested for HIV. This has eliminated the risk of contracting HIV from a blood transfusion.

How HIV Is Not Transmitted

HIV can be transmitted only through contact with certain body fluids, as described above. HIV cannot be spread through casual contact such as shaking hands, touching, hugging, or kissing. In families with an infected individual, HIV is *not* spread by sharing towels, combs, eating utensils, or bathroom facilities. HIV is *not* airborne, so it cannot be spread by coughing or sneezing, nor is it transmitted by the bites of insects such as mosquitoes.

Teens at Risk

Because sexually active teens tend to engage in high-risk behaviors, they are at serious risk for HIV/AIDS and other STDs. The U.S. Centers for Disease Control and Prevention, or CDC, gathers statistics on disease throughout the nation and the world. The following statistics clarify the threat posed by HIV for U.S. teens who engage in high-risk behaviors:

- In 2018, the number of new HIV infections totaled 37,832. Of these, 7,945 or more than 21 percent occurred in people between the ages of 13–24.
- According to the 2017 Youth Risk Behavior Surveillance System report, more than 39 percent of high school students report having had sexual intercourse.
- While condom use among teens who are sexually active has increased, one study shows that 40 percent of high school students report that they did not use a condom the last time they were sexually active.

HIV Prevention

In recent years, there has been progress in treating AIDS and AIDS-OIs. Many people are living symptom-free for longer than before. Today, a mother with HIV has a better chance of not transmitting it to her baby. People have become educated about the virus and are taking more precautions to protect themselves from coming in contact with it. Despite this progress, HIV/AIDS remains an incurable condition.

During your teen years, you may feel pressure to experiment with new behaviors, such as engaging in sexual activity and/or using alcohol or other drugs. Remember that your decisions can have an impact on the rest of your life. The only responsible decision is to choose abstinence from sexual activity, use condoms correctly if you are sexually active, and avoid all drug use, especially injection drug use. Here are some strategies to help you avoid pressure to engage in sexual activity or use drugs:

- Avoid situations in which pressure is certain. If you are at a party where you feel the situation is out of control, leave the party or call a parent or other trusted adult for help.
- Avoid being alone with a date in a private place. Avoid forming a dating relationship with someone whom you know to be sexually active.
- Avoid the use of alcohol and other drugs. Avoid known drug users and those who approve of drug use.
- When you use refusal strategies, be firm and unwavering. Use body language to reinforce your message.

What Is HIV/AIDS?

Health Skills Practice

Decision Making Have students use the decision-making process to evaluate the use of FDA-approved condoms and other contraceptives for pregnancy and STD prevention. Remind students to consider the options and the possible outcomes of each option along with the influence of values on the decision. Have students record their answers in their health journals. OL

Active Learning

Guest Speaker Invite a representative from the local health department to speak about HIV transmission and risk behaviors. Have each student prepare a brief essay describing what he or she learned from the speaker. OL

Reading Strategy

Emphasize Stress again that the most common ways HIV is spread—sexual intercourse and sharing IV needles—are choice- and behavior-related. Each individual has the opportunity to make healthful decisions to prevent the spread of HIV. OL

Caption Answer: *Sample answer: HIV is not spread by casual contact such as shaking hands or hugging.*

What Is HIV/AIDS?

Cultural Awareness

Ask students to discuss how HIV/AIDS education might help in the fight against HIV/AIDS. How might specific populations benefit from more widespread education? OL

Health Skills Practice

Accessing Information Stress to students that, as research on HIV/AIDS continues, information about HIV/AIDS is constantly changing. Reliable websites, such as the CDC, can be useful in ensuring that your information is up to date and accurate. OL

Caption Answer: *Sample answers: Avoid situations in which pressure is certain, avoid being alone with a date, avoid using alcohol and drugs, and be firm when using refusal strategies.*

ASSESS

Reteaching Have students use each of the vocabulary terms in a written sentence to explain how HIV is transmitted and the effect it has on the body. Have students form groups to share sentences. Discuss any discrepancies.

Enrichment Have students find information about the spread of HIV in other countries. Have them share their findings with the class.

Sum up the lesson by telling students that anyone can get HIV, regardless of race, gender, and sexual orientation. Ask students to explain the ways teens can make responsible decisions about risky behaviors to avoid infection.

Q&A
How can sexually active adults reduce the risk of HIV infection?
Sexually active individuals can take steps to reduce the risk of contracting HIV during sexual intercourse. Having only one partner who is, to the best of their knowledge, not infected with HIV reduces the risk. It is also important to use latex condoms properly during sexual intercourse. Properly used, latex condoms can prevent HIV transmission.

Staying Informed
You can find many sources of dependable information about HIV infection and AIDS. Reputable newspapers, magazines, and health segments on television and radio programs offer the latest scientific findings. Reliable sites on the Internet, such as government agencies and medical associations, also offer accurate updates. Many people, such as health care professionals and school counselors, are knowledgeable in this area. They can provide guidance in locating other reliable information sources.

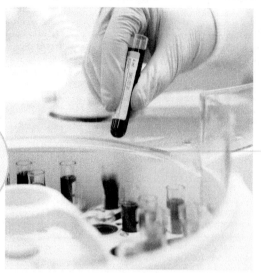

Blood that is donated in the United States is tested for HIV. **What three strategies can help teens avoid pressure to engage in high-risk behaviors?**

Lesson 1 Review

Facts and Vocabulary

1. What is AIDS and how is it related to HIV?
2. Describe the asymptomatic stage of AIDS.
3. Explain the relationship between risk behaviors, unsafe situations, and HIV/AIDS. Explain the ways in which HIV is known to be transmitted.
4. Are all teens at serious risk for HIV/AIDS?

Thinking Critically

5. **Analyze.** Do you think an individual infected with HIV is responsible for informing others of the infection? Why or why not?
6. **Synthesize.** Why is AIDS a serious threat to public health?

Applying Health Skills

7. **Advocacy.** Explain why abstinence from alcohol, drugs, and sexual activity is the only method that is 100 percent effective in preventing HIV/AIDS. Create and describe a concept for a poster that tells teens how to avoid HIV infection. Poster concepts should also explain how to avoid high-risk situations that challenge teens' decisions to abstain from sexual activity and all drug use, especially injection drug use.

©Adam Gaultridge Matstock

116 HIV and AIDS

Lesson 1 Review Answers

1. AIDS is a fatal disorder with no fully effective treatment or known cure. AIDS is the final stage of infection with the human immunodeficiency virus (HIV), a virus that attacks the immune system.
2. This stage lasts for a span of 10 years or more. The virus is largely confined to the lymph nodes, where it invades and takes over or destroys helper T cells. There are no outward signs of the infection—the person looks and feels healthy.
3. The virus is borne in body fluids such as blood, semen, vaginal secretions, and breast milk. It is transmitted by activities or risk behaviors that cause a person to come in contact with these fluids from an infected person if there are breaks in the skin at the point of contact for the uninfected person.
4. No, only teens who are or have been sexually active and/or use or have used drugs, especially injection drugs, are at serious risk for HIV/AIDS.
5. Answers will vary.
6. Answers will vary but should include increasing numbers of people affected, lack of a cure, effects on victims and their families, and costs for health care.
7. Posters will vary, but should include strategies to avoid high-risk behaviors.

HIV/AIDS Testing and Treatment

BIG IDEA There are many options available today for diagnosing the presence of HIV/AIDS and receiving support.

QUICK WRITE

Create a two-column chart. In one column, list three or more conditions, careers, or other circumstances that make it important for people to be tested for HIV. Explain your reason for each in the second column.

Detecting HIV Antibodies

Within a few years of the diagnosis of the first cases of AIDS in the United States, tests were developed to detect HIV infection. Currently, all donated blood must be tested for HIV. Anyone who donates body organs or tissue, as well as people who join the armed forces, must undergo testing. Medical workers also must undergo testing after occupational exposure to HIV.

When HIV enters a person's body, the immune system produces antibodies to destroy the pathogen. Unfortunately, the antibodies produced in response to HIV are unable to completely eliminate the virus from the body. HIV tests can detect these antibodies, however. This makes the antibodies very useful for diagnosis. It takes an average of 25 days for detectable antibodies to develop. However, detectable antibodies may take six months or longer to develop in some people.

BEFORE YOU READ

Organize Information. Create a graphic organizer showing ways that HIV/AIDS is diagnosed and treated.

Vocabulary

rapid test
antibody screening test
pneumocystis carinii pneumonia (PCP)
Kaposi's sarcoma (KS)
cytomegalovirus (CMV)
candidiasis
community outreach program
grief counselor

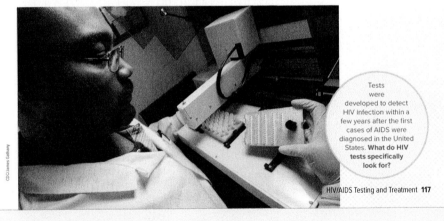

Tests were developed to detect HIV infection within a few years after the first cases of AIDS were diagnosed in the United States. **What do HIV tests specifically look for?**

HIV/AIDS Testing and Treatment **117**

CDC/James Gathany

LESSON 2
HIV/AIDS Testing and Treatment

FOCUS

BIG IDEA There are many options available today for diagnosing the presence of HIV/AIDS and receiving support. Tell students that people with HIV/AIDS need more than just health care. They often need practical help, such as legal and social services, as well as a variety of other community services such as hospice or grief counseling.

Reading Strategy

Organize Information Students' questions will vary.

QUICKWRITE

Before students answer, write the following on the board for students to answer: *What kinds of care and help might a person infected with HIV/AIDS need?* **Accept reasonable responses.**

Student Objectives:

- Describe the tests that are used to diagnose the presence of HIV antibodies.
- Identify the symptoms and medications associated with HIV and AIDS.
- Identify HIV/AIDS support services available in the community.

TEACH

Reading Strategy

Discussing Review the symptoms of HIV infection with the class. Ask students what other conditions besides HIV infection might cause the same symptoms. **Answer: diseases of the blood, pregnancy, presence of other diseases.** Emphasize that whenever symptoms are present for any length of time, a person should visit a health care professional for diagnosis and treatment of whatever is causing the symptoms. OL

Caption Answer: *HIV tests detect the presence of antibodies produced by the immune system in response to the virus.*

HIV/AIDS Testing and Treatment

Critical Thinking

Occupational Exposure Ask students what *occupational exposure to HIV* means. How might medical workers be exposed to HIV infection? OL

Reading Strategy

Emphasize At this time, it might be useful to have students review the stages of HIV infection section in Lesson 1. BL

Active Learning

Research Have students find out how HIV tests are performed. Ask them to explain which bodily fluids can be tested for HIV. Have students call a local testing facility to find out what type of fluid is tested. AL

Class Activity Have students go to the library and research Elizabeth Glaser, who in 1988 co-founded the Pediatric AIDS Foundation after Elizabeth and her husband, Paul, found out that she and their two children were infected with HIV. Ask students to discuss why children infected with HIV might need different treatment than adults infected with the virus. OL

Did You Know?

Certain factors can lead to a false-reactive antibody screening test:

- Laboratory error. Samples are sometimes incorrectly labeled, or a nonreactive sample is accidentally contaminated by a nearby reactive sample.
- Blood abnormalities. Diseases of the blood have been linked to false-reactive tests.
- Pregnancy. Women in a second or later pregnancy may have false-reactive readings.
- Other conditions. People who have certain conditions such as Lyme disease, syphilis, or lupus may have false-reactive readings.
- Cross-reactivity with other retroviruses. Although every virus is different, some viruses have similar genetic makeups. For example, human T cell lymphoma/leukemia viruses (HTLV) have structures similar to that of HIV and therefore produce similar antibodies.

Types of Laboratory HIV Tests

After collecting samples and sending them to a laboratory, technicians screen the samples for HIV antibodies. These antibodies do not occur naturally in a person's body; they are produced only in the presence of an infection. The most common laboratory tests used for HIV screening are the nucleic acid test (NAT), antigen/antibody screening tests, and rapid antibody screening tests. Three types of **rapid tests** can be used. They are the rapid antibody screening test, the oral fluid antibody self-test, and the home collection kit.

A NAT test looks for the presence of the virus in the blood. This test is expensive and is generally used only when a person has recently been in a high-risk situation, or if the person is displaying early signs of HIV infection. When the NAT test is used, an antigen/antibody test is usually done at the same time.

Antigen/antibody screening test. This test looks for the presence of HIV antigens and antibodies in the blood. Antigens are foreign substances in the blood. They cause the immune system to become active. If the results are positive, that means HIV antibodies are present.

One of three types of rapid tests may be used in situations where the infected person might not come back to learn the results of an HIV test. With the rapid antibody screening test, a small sample of blood or oral fluid is used. A home collection kit is similar. A small sample of blood is collected at home and then sent to a laboratory where it is tested. Another test is the oral fluid antibody self-test. This test produces results in 20 minutes, and may be used at home, at a community testing center, or in a clinic.

Follow-up Tests. If a test for HIV is returned showing a positive result, an additional test is done to confirm the first test. Further testing is also done to distinguish the type of HIV antibodies, and to look directly at the virus.

Cost of Testing. HIV testing is fully covered by health insurance. To help prevent the spread of HIV, public health departments will offer the test free-of-charge. The local public health department can provide information on free testing, and may offer locations for free tests on the agency's website.

Symptoms of HIV Infection

Many people have no early symptoms when they are infected with HIV, but some develop flu-like symptoms a month or two after they are infected. These symptoms include fever, headache, fatigue, and swollen lymph nodes. Within one to four weeks, these symptoms usually disappear.

A few months to ten years later (or longer), an infected person may develop other symptoms. These include persistent swollen glands, lack of energy, weight loss, frequent fevers and sweats, persistent or frequent yeast infections, skin rashes, and short-term memory loss.

Diagnosis of AIDS

The current CDC definition of AIDS requires that a person be HIV positive and have either a helper T cell count below 200 or at least one AIDS-OI. These are some of the most common AIDS-OIs:

- **Pneumocystis carinii pneumonia (PCP).** This is a fungal infection that causes a form of pneumonia .This is the most common cause of pneumonia in people with AIDS; symptoms include difficulty breathing, fever, a dry cough, weakness, and weight loss.

- **Kaposi's sarcoma (KS).** KS is a kind of cancer that develops in connective tissues. KS usually appears on the skin or in the lining of the mouth, nose, or anus. More serious cases involve the lungs, liver, gastrointestinal tract, and lymph nodes. KS causes flat, painless skin lesions that look like bruises.

REAL WORLD CONNECTION

The Cost of HIV/AIDS

The cost of HIV/AIDS in terms of suffering and death is immeasurable. Fortunately, mortality rates in the United States continue to decline. The rate of spending on HIV/AIDS-related issues is not declining, however. Look at the chart below. Which does the government spend more on each year: health care, research, or prevention? Has spending increased more significantly for one area than for another?

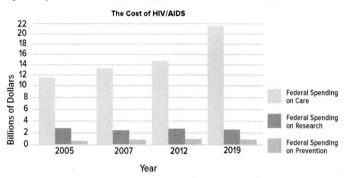

The Cost of HIV/AIDS

Source: CDC. Div. of HIV/AIDS Prevention, Maximizing Impact, DHAP Annual Report 2012; Kaiser Family Foundation, 2019.

Activity: Research

An estimated 7,945 cases of HIV/AIDS in people in the United States ages 13 through 24 were reported to the CDC in 2018. Research the number of cases reported and the amount of government spending on one other type of STD. Create a graph that compares your findings on the cost of STDs to the cost of HIV/AIDS.

HIV/AIDS Testing and Treatment **119**

REAL WORLD CONNECTION

The Cost of HIV/AIDS Point out to students the source of this information on the cost of HIV/AIDS. Ask whether they consider this a reliable source of information. Then have volunteers explain why or why not. OL

Reading Strategy

Building Vocabulary Point out that many of the vocabulary terms are the names of diseases. Ask students why they think so many of these names also have shortened forms. **They are long, with many syllables, and might be difficult for people to pronounce and remember. Shortened forms might sound less threatening.** OL EL

HIV/AIDS Testing and Treatment

Health Skills Practice

Accessing Information Have students work in small groups to research and identify local resources concerning reproductive and sexual health. This can include clinics where they can get information about all FDA-approved contraceptives, HIV/STD testing, and other reproductive medical care. Students could use a local online or print directory as a source. Have groups share what they learned with the class. OL

Reading Strategy

Emphasize Stress to students that drugs to fight the symptoms of HIV/AIDS are treatments, not cures. Although they can slow its progress, they do not rid the body of HIV. OL

Caption Answer: *The drugs have strong side effects, they can be very expensive, and they are often difficult to manage.*

- **Cytomegalovirus (CMV).** This is a virus found in 50 percent of the general population and 90 percent of people with HIV. A weakened immune system allows this opportunistic infection to develop, and it can cause blindness, pneumonia, and gastrointestinal disease.

- **Candidiasis.** This is an infection caused by a common type of yeast (fungus) found in almost everyone in the general population. Genital candidiasis occurs when there is an overgrowth of the fungus Candida. Candidiasis can also affect the mouth (thrush) or the throat (esophagitis). Candidiasis of the respiratory tract, trachea, or lungs is related to AIDS.

Research and Treatment

As yet, there is no cure for HIV infection or AIDS. Much progress has been made, however, in delaying the onset of AIDS and in treating AIDS-OIs.

Drug Research

Antiretroviral drugs inhibit HIV from making copies of itself. The first such drugs developed to fight HIV were zidovudine (AZT), didanosine (ddI), and zalcitabine (ddC). These drugs, known collectively as nucleoside reverse transcriptase inhibitors (NRTIs), are still being used today.

Another class of drugs, called protease inhibitors (PIs), blocks the progress of HIV in later stages of reproduction within the body. Examples of these drugs are saquinavir, ritonavir, indinavir, and nelfinavir.

Yet a third class of drugs, known as non-nucleoside reverse transcriptase inhibitors (NNRTIs), has also been added to the list of drugs used against AIDS. Examples of these drugs are nevirapine, delavirdine, and efavirenz. Like NRTIs, these drugs keep HIV from infecting new cells. Unfortunately, HIV quickly becomes resistant to NNRTIs when they are used alone.

Researchers have made progress in treating AIDS, but there is no cure for HIV infection or AIDS. **What are some of the drawbacks to the drugs used to treat AIDS?**

Scientists now know that taking a combination of drugs, sometimes referred to as a cocktail, is more effective than taking one drug alone. An assortment of drugs can minimize side effects and prevent HIV from becoming resistant to individual drugs. The current recommended treatment for HIV is a triple-drug combination known as highly active antiretroviral therapy, or HAART. Combinations of NRTIs, PIs, and NNRTIs are used in this regimen.

Drugs are said to be working if the level of virus in the blood decreases. By using a combination of drugs, some individuals are able to decrease their viral load to such an extent that it is undetectable in blood tests.

While combination-drug therapy has helped individuals infected with HIV/AIDS, there are many drawbacks to these drugs. AIDS drugs have very strong side effects, including nausea, vomiting, diarrhea, headaches, and intestinal distress. They are also very expensive, costing in the range of $12,000 to $20,000 a year in the United States.

In addition, the regimen of drugs can be difficult to manage. Some combinations require as many as 20 pills a day that must be taken on a very rigid schedule. Today, however, there are simpler drug regimens available to some, with only one to three pills that have to be taken once or twice daily. Despite progress in treatment, AIDS remains a difficult and fatal disease.

Vaccines

Medical researchers began trials on HIV vaccines in 1987. Since then, almost 60 vaccines have been studied worldwide. The original focus involved finding a protein that would cause the immune system to produce effective HIV antibodies. Research has expanded to include ways to stimulate production of killer T cells to help fight off HIV infection. Researchers are studying live bacteria and viruses, as well as chemically synthesized HIV proteins, killed or weakened HIV, and manipulated genetic material.

Support From The Community

People with HIV/AIDS need medical care, but they also need other kinds of support to help them cope with their illness. Extra support often comes from **community outreach programs.** These programs are organizations, largely staffed by volunteers, which provide a wide range of essential services to HIV/AIDS patients, their families, and their loved ones. Community outreach programs can provide these services:

- **Practical assistance.** People with HIV/AIDS often need help finding housing as well as getting legal, social, mental health, and visiting-nurse services. Individuals with advanced AIDS-OIs may need help making meals.

Community outreach programs include events such as walks that promote awareness of HIV/AIDS prevention and treatment. **How might support networks be helpful to people with HIV/AIDS and their families?**

HIV/AIDS Testing and Treatment **121**

LESSON 2
HIV/AIDS Testing and Treatment

Critical Thinking

Discuss Have students discuss ways that a support system can benefit people with HIV/AIDS. BL

Reading Strategy

Cures and Vaccines Discuss with the class the difference between a cure and a vaccine. **A cure heals those who have contracted a disease. A vaccine immunizes people who have not contracted a disease, preventing them from ever becoming infected.** OL

Critical Thinking

Social Health Ask students to think about how being diagnosed with HIV/AIDS might affect a person's family and friends. What types of support might these people need? OL

Active Learning

Class Activity Have students find out what services are available locally for people with HIV/AIDS. Remind students to include testing facilities, health care providers, and legal and counseling services. Ask them to create a chart listing the services with descriptions and contact information. Display the charts in the classroom. OL

Caption Answer: *Answers may vary, but could include: help finding housing; legal, social, mental health, and nurse services; help making meals.*

HIV/AIDS Testing and Treatment

ASSESS

Reteaching Put the following headings on the board: *PCP, KS, CMV,* and *Candidiasis.* Have students list facts about each disease under its heading. If necessary, have students reread the section "Diagnosis of AIDS" to locate the facts.

Enrichment Have students do research to find out about the "Declaration of Commitment on HIV/AIDS" issued by the United Nations in 2001 and the "Declaration of Commitment on HIV/AIDS: Five Years Later," issued in 2006. Ask them to write a brief report about the declarations and why the United Nations is involved with HIV/AIDS.

Sum up the lesson by asking students to list the three most important things they learned about HIV testing and treatment.

Q&A
What are the major obstacles to research and treatment of HIV/AIDS?
Because HIV is constantly undergoing changes in its genetic structure, the virus has been able to build up resistance to medications. Also, several new strains of HIV have developed, further complicating the search for a vaccine. The treatments that have been developed are very expensive, and some people cannot afford them. In addition, some individuals find it difficult to follow a rigid schedule for taking so many medicines—often with unpleasant side effects—each day.

- **One-on-one support.** As HIV/AIDS progresses, individuals with AIDS may need help with daily activities such as shopping, cooking, and cleaning. Some groups establish a buddy system in which a volunteer helps an individual with daily chores and provides companionship and moral support.

- **Crisis counseling.** Crisis counselors help individuals cope with problems when they feel overwhelmed or out of control.

- **Grief counseling.** Most people with HIV/AIDS face a painful, lengthy illness. A **grief counselor** is a professional who is trained to help people deal with the issues of sickness, dying, and death. A grief counselor can help individuals and their families and loved ones cope with and adjust to the realities of various AIDS-OIs.

- **Information dissemination.** Those infected with HIV need a way to obtain and interpret the latest accurate information on the treatment and care of HIV/AIDS. Many community outreach programs sponsor an AIDS telephone hotline that people can call if they have questions. Some groups, particularly in larger cities, publish newsletters. The San Francisco-based Project Inform sponsors meetings throughout the United States to keep people up to date on the latest information. The CDC keeps a list of community support groups and maintains an AIDS hotline of its own.

Lesson 2 Review

Facts and Vocabulary

1. What do HIV tests detect?

2. What precautions should a person take if his or her first test results for HIV antibodies are negative?

3. What does the current CDC definition of AIDS require?

4. Why is a combination of drugs used to treat HIV infection?

5. Identify and describe some of the services provided by community outreach programs for individuals with HIV/AIDS and their families.

Thinking Critically

6. **Compare.** Explain how technology has impacted the health status of individuals with HIV/AIDS. How are the EIA and Western blot tests used?

7. **Analyze.** Why do you think some people with HIV don't use the recommended combinations of drugs?

Applying Health Skills

8. **Advocacy.** Outline a plan for a community outreach program that provides support to people with HIV/AIDS. Provide descriptions of the services that will be provided and information on how teens might get the word out about these services. Include a statement or slogan that would help convince others to join the program and give of their time and talents to help those in need.

Lesson 2 Review Answers

1. The tests detect HIV antibodies.
2. He or she should not engage in activities that can transmit HIV until testing at six months after exposure is also negative.
3. It requires that a person be HIV positive *and* have *either* a helper T cell count below 200 *or* the presence of at least one AIDS-OI.
4. An assortment of drugs can minimize side effects and prevent HIV from becoming resistant to individual drugs.
5. They provide practical assistance, one-on-one support, crisis counseling, grief counseling, and information dissemination.
6. The antibody screening test is a screening tool used to detect the presence of antibodies for HIV in the blood. If the results of this test are positive two times, a confirmatory test such as the Western blot is done. If this test is positive, a person is considered to be infected with HIV.
7. Answers will vary, but may include that individuals can't afford it, don't like the side effects, or don't have enough information about it to get treatment.
8. Plans will vary. Students should include descriptions of local services and ways to encourage others to participate.

Reviewing Facts and Vocabulary

1. How does HIV destroy the immune system?

2. What are *AIDS-opportunistic illnesses*?

3. What is the main way HIV is spread?

4. List three ways HIV is not transmitted.

5. HIV/AIDS is not curable, but it is preventable. What are the best methods of prevention for teens?

6. List possible early symptoms of HIV. How long do they usually last?

7. How long can HIV stay in the body before a person shows symptoms of infection?

8. What is *Kaposi's sarcoma*? What parts of the body are affected in serious cases?

9. How do antiretroviral drugs work?

10. What are *community outreach programs*?

Writing Critically

11. Synthesize. Write an essay explaining why you think many people are uninformed about HIV infection and AIDS.

12. Evaluate. Write a paragraph on whether you believe that people should be required to undergo a test for AIDS before being considered for employment or medical insurance. Explain your reasoning.

13. Analyze. Write a summary analyzing the importance of abstinence from all sexual activity before marriage in reducing the risk of contracting HIV/AIDS. Explain why abstinence from alcohol, drugs, and sexual activity is the only method that is 100 percent effective in preventing HIV/AIDS.

14. Apply. Write a summary explaining the relationship between risk behaviors and HIV/AIDS. A person has been engaging in behaviors that can lead to HIV infection. He has been tested for HIV and the result was negative. What should he do next?

Applying Health Skills

15. Communication Skills. With your parents or guardians, discuss whether you feel HIV testing should be required for health care providers.

16. Refusal Skills. What refusal strategies would you advise a teen to use if her peers were pressuring her to try using an injection drug just one time?

BEYOND THE CLASSROOM ACTIVITIES

PARENT INVOLVEMENT
Treating Disease. At present, HIV/AIDS is incurable. Many diseases throughout history were also incurable until medical researchers found a way to combat them. With your parent or guardian, choose one of the following diseases and write a report on its history: polio, tuberculosis, pneumonia, bubonic plague, malaria.

SCHOOL AND COMMUNITY
Local Support. Find out what organizations in your community are helping people with AIDS. Make a list of these organizations, and describe specific steps each is taking to help those suffering from AIDS.

BEYOND THE CLASSROOM

Parent Involvement: Treating Disease. At present, HIV/AIDS is incurable. Many diseases throughout history were also incurable until medical researchers found a way to combat them. Have students choose of the following diseases with a parent or guardian and write a report on its history: polio, tuberculosis, pneumonia, bubonic plague, malaria.

School and Community: Local Support. Direct students to find out what organizations in their community are helping people with AIDS. Have students make a list of these organizations, and describe specific steps each is taking to help those suffering from AIDS.

- Encourage students to participate in activities that involve parents and the community.
- Discussions may include issues of increased risk of contracting HIV infection, public health, and confidentiality.
- Answers will vary but should include saying "no" firmly and leaving.

Assessment Answers

1. HIV enters certain cells, including helper T-cells, and reproduces itself. As more cells become infected, more are destroyed and the immune system weakens. The body succumbs to AIDS-opportunistic illnesses.

2. They are illnesses the body could normally fight off if the immune system were healthy.

3. The main way is through unprotected sexual activity with an infected partner.

4. Any three of the following: through shaking hands, touching, or hugging; by sharing towels, combs, eating utensils, or bathroom facilities; by coughing or sneezing; by the bites of insects such as mosquitoes.

5. The best methods of prevention of HIV/AIDS involve avoiding risk behaviors—for teens, abstinence from sexual activity before marriage and avoidance of all drug use, especially injection drug use.

6. They are flulike symptoms including fever, headache, fatigue, and swollen lymph nodes. They usually disappear within one to four weeks.

7. HIV can remain in the body for a span of years before symptoms appear.

8. It is a kind of cancer that develops in connective tissues, usually in the skin or in the linings of the mouth, nose, or anus. In more serious cases it involves the lungs, liver, gastrointestinal tract, and lymph nodes.

9. They inhibit HIV from making copies of itself.

10. They are organizations, staffed largely by volunteers, that provide a wide range of essential services to HIV/AIDS patients, their families, and their loved ones.

11. Answers will vary but may include that people only know what they've heard from other people, they have not read scientific or factual articles, or they believe in certain stereotypes that keep them from learning the facts.

12. Answers will vary, but students should provide explanations for their opinions.

13. Answers will vary, but students should provide explanations for their opinions.

14. The person should avoid behaviors known to transmit HIV for six months and be retested.

15. Responses will vary.

16. Answers will vary.

GLOSSARY/GLOSARIO

English

Abortion Any termination of a pregnancy.

Abstinence A deliberate decision to avoid harmful behaviors, including sexual activity and the use of alcohol, tobacco, and other drugs.

Acquaintance rape Rape by someone the victim knows.

Acquired Immune Deficiency Syndrome (AIDS) A potentially fatal disorder that interferes with the body's natural ability to fight infection. AIDS is the final stage of infection caused by the human immunodeficiency virus (HIV).

Affirmative consent The clear and voluntary agreement to engage in sexual activity.

AIDS-opportunistic illnesses (AIDS-OIs) Infections the body could fight off if the immune system were healthy.

Amniocentesis A procedure that reveals chromosomal abnormalities and certain metabolic disorders in the fetus.

Amniotic sac A fluid-filled sac that surrounds the embryo.

Antibodies Proteins that help destroy pathogens that enter the body.

Antibody screening test A test used to detect the presence of antibodies for HIV in blood.

Bacterial vaginosis (BV) A type of vaginitis caused by an imbalance of bacteria normally found in the vagina.

Birth defect An abnormality in the structure or function of the body that is present at birth. Birth defects can be caused by abnormal genes or by environmental factors.

Birthing centers Facilities that have homelike settings, are separate from a hospital, and offer medication-free births.

Bisexual Someone who is sexually attracted to people of both genders.

Blastocyst A ball of cells with a cavity in the center.

Blended family A family consisting of two married adults who have children from a previous marriage living with them.

Español

Aborto Cualquier interrupción de un embarazo.

Abstinencia Una decisión consciente de evitar la conducta peligrosa, como las relaciones sexuales y el uso del alcohol, tabaco y otras drogas.

Violación por un conocido Una violación perpetrada por alguien a quien la víctima conoce.

Síndrome de inmunodeficiencia adquirida (SIDA) Una afección potencialmente mortal que interfiere con la habilidad natural del cuerpo de combatir infecciones. El SIDA es la etapa final de la infección causada por el virus de la inmunodeficiencia humana (VIH).

Consentimiento afirmativo El acuerdo claro y voluntario de participar en actividades sexuales.

Enfermedades oportunistas del SIDA (EO del SIDA) Infecciones que el cuerpo podría combatir si el sistema inmune estuviera sano.

Amniocentesis Procedimiento que muestra anormalidades en los cromosomas de un feto y ciertos trastornos metabólicos.

Amnios Saco lleno de líquido que rodea el embrión.

Anticuerpos Proteínas que ayudan a destruir los patógenos gérmenes que entran en el cuerpo.

Prueba de detección de anticuerpos Prueba para detectar la presencia de anticuerpos contra el VIH en la sangre.

Vaginosis bacteriana Un tipo de vaginosis causada por el desequilibrio de bacterias que normalmente están en la vagina.

Defecto de nacimiento Anormalidad en la estructura o fun- ción del cuerpo que está presente al nacimiento. Puede ser el resulto de genes anormales o de factores ambientales.

Centros de parto natural Instalaciones que tienen un ambi- ente hogareño, están separados de los hospitales y ofrecen partos sin medicación.

Bisexual Alguien que siente atracción sexual por personas de ambos géneros.

Blastocisto Un balón de células con una cavidad en el centro.

Familia mixta Una familia en que se casan dos adultos que tienen hijos de un matrimonio anterior viviendo con ellos

Reviewing Facts and Vocabulary

1. How does HIV destroy the immune system?

2. What are *AIDS-opportunistic illnesses*?

3. What is the main way HIV is spread?

4. List three ways HIV is not transmitted.

5. HIV/AIDS is not curable, but it is preventable. What are the best methods of prevention for teens?

6. List possible early symptoms of HIV. How long do they usually last?

7. How long can HIV stay in the body before a person shows symptoms of infection?

8. What is *Kaposi's sarcoma*? What parts of the body are affected in serious cases?

9. How do antiretroviral drugs work?

10. What are *community outreach programs*?

Writing Critically

11. Synthesize. Write an essay explaining why you think many people are uninformed about HIV infection and AIDS.

12. Evaluate. Write a paragraph on whether you believe that people should be required to undergo a test for AIDS before being considered for employment or medical insurance. Explain your reasoning.

13. Analyze. Write a summary analyzing the importance of abstinence from all sexual activity before marriage in reducing the risk of contracting HIV/AIDS. Explain why abstinence from alcohol, drugs, and sexual activity is the only method that is 100 percent effective in preventing HIV/AIDS.

14. Apply. Write a summary explaining the relationship between risk behaviors and HIV/AIDS. A person has been engaging in behaviors that can lead to HIV infection. He has been tested for HIV and the result was negative. What should he do next?

Applying Health Skills

15. Communication Skills. With your parents or guardians, discuss whether you feel HIV testing should be required for health care providers.

16. Refusal Skills. What refusal strategies would you advise a teen to use if her peers were pressuring her to try using an injection drug just one time?

BEYOND THE CLASSROOM ACTIVITIES

PARENT INVOLVEMENT

Treating Disease. At present, HIV/AIDS is incurable. Many diseases throughout history were also incurable until medical researchers found a way to combat them. With your parent or guardian, choose one of the following diseases and write a report on its history: polio, tuberculosis, pneumonia, bubonic plague, malaria.

SCHOOL AND COMMUNITY

Local Support. Find out what organizations in your community are helping people with AIDS. Make a list of these organizations, and describe specific steps each is taking to help those suffering from AIDS.

Assessment **123**

BEYOND THE CLASSROOM

Parent Involvement: Treating Disease. At present, HIV/AIDS is incurable. Many diseases throughout history were also incurable until medical researchers found a way to combat them. Have students choose of the following diseases with a parent or guardian and write a report on its history: polio, tuberculosis, pneumonia, bubonic plague, malaria.

School and Community: Local Support. Direct students to find out what organizations in their community are helping people with AIDS. Have students make a list of these organizations, and describe specific steps each is taking to help those suffering from AIDS.

- Encourage students to participate in activities that involve parents and the community.

- Discussions may include issues of increased risk of contracting HIV infection, public health, and confidentiality.

- Answers will vary but should include saying "no" firmly and leaving.

Assessment Answers

1. HIV enters certain cells, including helper T-cells, and reproduces itself. As more cells become infected, more are destroyed and the immune system weakens. The body succumbs to AIDS-opportunistic illnesses.

2. They are illnesses the body could normally fight off if the immune system were healthy.

3. The main way is through unprotected sexual activity with an infected partner.

4. Any three of the following: through shaking hands, touching, or hugging; by sharing towels, combs, eating utensils, or bathroom facilities; by coughing or sneezing; by the bites of insects such as mosquitoes.

5. The best methods of prevention of HIV/AIDS involve avoiding risk behaviors—for teens, abstinence from sexual activity before marriage and avoidance of all drug use, especially injection drug use.

6. They are flulike symptoms including fever, headache, fatigue, and swollen lymph nodes. They usually disappear within one to four weeks.

7. HIV can remain in the body for a span of years before symptoms appear.

8. It is a kind of cancer that develops in connective tissues, usually in the skin or in the linings of the mouth, nose, or anus. In more serious cases it involves the lungs, liver, gastrointestinal tract, and lymph nodes.

9. They inhibit HIV from making copies of itself.

10. They are organizations, staffed largely by volunteers, that provide a wide range of essential services to HIV/AIDS patients, their families, and their loved ones.

11. Answers will vary but may include that people only know what they've heard from other people, they have not read scientific or factual articles, or they believe in certain stereotypes that keep them from learning the facts.

12. Answers will vary, but students should provide explanations for their opinions.

13. Answers will vary, but students should provide explanations for their opinions.

14. The person should avoid behaviors known to transmit HIV for six months and be retested.

15. Responses will vary.

16. Answers will vary.

English

A

Español

Abortion Any termination of a pregnancy.

Abstinence A deliberate decision to avoid harmful behaviors, including sexual activity and the use of alcohol, tobacco, and other drugs.

Acquaintance rape Rape by someone the victim knows.

Acquired Immune Deficiency Syndrome (AIDS) A potentially fatal disorder that interferes with the body's natural ability to fight infection. AIDS is the final stage of infection caused by the human immunodeficiency virus (HIV).

Affirmative consent The clear and voluntary agreement to engage in sexual activity.

AIDS-opportunistic illnesses (AIDS-OIs) Infections the body could fight off if the immune system were healthy.

Amniocentesis A procedure that reveals chromosomal abnormalities and certain metabolic disorders in the fetus.

Amniotic sac A fluid-filled sac that surrounds the embryo.

Antibodies Proteins that help destroy pathogens that enter the body.

Antibody screening test A test used to detect the presence of antibodies for HIV in blood.

Aborto Cualquier interrupción de un embarazo.

Abstinencia Una decisión consciente de evitar la conducta peligrosa, como las relaciones sexuales y el uso del alcohol, tabaco y otras drogas.

Violación por un conocido Una violación perpetrada por alguien a quien la víctima conoce.

Síndrome de inmunodeficiencia adquirida (SIDA) Una afección potencialmente mortal que interfiere con la habilidad natural del cuerpo de combatir infecciones. El SIDA es la etapa final de la infección causada por el virus de la inmunodeficiencia humana (VIH).

Consentimiento afirmativo El acuerdo claro y voluntario de participar en actividades sexuales.

Enfermedades oportunistas del SIDA (EO del SIDA) Infecciones que el cuerpo podría combatir si el sistema inmune estuviera sano.

Amniocentesis Procedimiento que muestra anormalidades en los cromosomas de un feto y ciertos trastornos metabólicos.

Amnios Saco lleno de líquido que rodea el embrión.

Anticuerpos Proteínas que ayudan a destruir los patógenos gérmenes que entran en el cuerpo.

Prueba de detección de anticuerpos Prueba para detectar la presencia de anticuerpos contra el VIH en la sangre.

B

Bacterial vaginosis (BV) A type of vaginitis caused by an imbalance of bacteria normally found in the vagina.

Birth defect An abnormality in the structure or function of the body that is present at birth. Birth defects can be caused by abnormal genes or by environmental factors.

Birthing centers Facilities that have homelike settings, are separate from a hospital, and offer medication-free births.

Bisexual Someone who is sexually attracted to people of both genders.

Blastocyst A ball of cells with a cavity in the center.

Blended family A family consisting of two married adults who have children from a previous marriage living with them.

Vaginosis bacteriana Un tipo de vaginosis causada por el desequilibrio de bacterias que normalmente están en la vagina.

Defecto de nacimiento Anormalidad en la estructura o fun- ción del cuerpo que está presente al nacimiento. Puede ser el resulto de genes anormales o de factores ambientales.

Centros de parto natural Instalaciones que tienen un ambi- ente hogareño, están separados de los hospitales y ofrecen partos sin medicación.

Bisexual Alguien que siente atracción sexual por personas de ambos géneros.

Blastocisto Un balón de células con una cavidad en el centro.

Familia mixta Una familia en que se casan dos adultos que tienen hijos de un matrimonio anterior viviendo con ellos

English

Español

C

Candidiasis An infection caused by a common type of yeast (fungus) found in almost everyone in the general population.

Candidiasis Infección por un tipo común de levadura (hongos) que está presente en casi toda la gente.

Cervical cap A thimble-shaped, soft latex cup that fits snugly over the cervix, as a method of birth control.

Tapón cervical Una tapa de látex blanda en forma de dedal que se calza por encima de la apertura del útero o cérvix.

Cervix The neck of the uterus.

Cerviz Cuello del útero.

Cesarean birth A method of childbirth in which a surgical incision is made through the abdominal wall and uterus. The baby is lifted out through the surgical incision.

Parto por cesárea Un método de parto en el que se hace una incisión quirúrgica a través de la pared abdominal y el útero. El bebé se saca a través de la incisión.

Chlamydia An STD that is caused by the bacterium Chlamydia trachomatis.

Clamidia Una enfermedad de transmisión sexual causada por la bacteria Chlamydia trachomatis.

Chorionic villi sampling (CVS) A test used to reveal genetic disorders and fetal age and gender.

Biopsia de vellosidades coriónicas Prueba utilizada para mostrar trastornos genéticos y la edad y el género del feto.

Cognitive Relating to the ability to reason and think out abstract solutions.

Cognitivo Referente a la capacidad para pensar y llegar a soluciones abstractas.

Commitment A promise or a pledge.

Compromiso Un acuerdo o promesa.

Communication The process through which you send messages to and receive messages from others.

Comunicación Proceso por el cual envías mensajes y recibes mensajes de otros.

Community outreach programs Organizations, largely staffed by volunteers, which provide a wide range of essential services to HIV/AIDS patients, their families, and their loved ones.

Programas para ayudar a la comunidad Organizaciones dirigidas mayormente por voluntarios quienes proveen servi- cios esenciales para las personas con VIH/SIDA, sus familias y otros seres queridos.

Condom A thin sheath of latex, plastic, or animal tissue that is placed on the erect penis to catch semen. It is a physical barrier to the passage of sperm into the vagina and toward the ovum.

Condón Una lámina fina de plástico, látex o tejido animal que se coloca en el pene erecto para recoger semen. Actúa como una barrera física, impidiendo que el semen entre en la vagina o pase hacia el óvulo.

Conflict A disagreement, struggle, or fight.

Conflicto Desacuerdo, lucha o pelea.

Consent Permission or agreement for something to happen.

Consentimiento Permiso o acuerdo para que algo suceda.

Contraception Prevention of pregnancy.

Anticoncepción La prevención de embarazos.

Contraceptive injection A birth control procedure in which a female receives an injection once every three months to prevent ovulation.

Inyección anticonceptivo Un proceso anticonceptivo en el cual una mujer recibe una inyección una vez cada tres meses para prevenir la ovulación.

Cytomegalovirus (CMV) A virus found in 50 percent of the general population and 90 percent of people with HIV.

Citomegalovirus (CMV) Virus que se encuentra en 50 por ciento del gran público y en 90 por ciento de la gente con VIH.

D

Date rape Rape by someone the victim is dating.

Violación durante una cita (violación a escondidas) Violación por alguien con quien la víctima sale.

Developmental tasks An event that needs to occur during a particular age period for a person to continue his or her growth toward becoming a healthy, mature adult.

Tareas requeridas para el desarrollo Un suceso que tiene que ocurrir a una edad determinada para que la persona pueda continuar su desarrollo hasta la madurez saludable.

Diaphragm A soft latex or silicone cup with a flexible rim that covers the entrance to the cervix, as a method of birth control.

Diafragma Un disco de látex o silicio blando con borde flexible que cubre la apertura del útero.

GLOSSARY/GLOSARIO

English

Español

E

Egg cells A reproductive cell from the female that joins with a sperm cell to make a new life.

Óvulos Célula reproductora feminina que se une con el espermatooide para crear una nueva vida.

Ejaculation The release of semen from the penis.

Eyaculación Salida del semen del pene.

Embryo An implanted blastocyst from the time of implantation until about the eighth week of development.

Embrión Un blastocisto implantado, desde el momento de implantación hasta aproximadamente la octava semana de desarrollo.

Empathy The ability to feel what others feel, to put yourself in someone else's place.

Empatía La capacidad de sentir lo que otros sienten, de ponerse en el lugar de otro.

Endocrine system A body system made up of ductless glands that secrete chemicals called hormones into the blood.

Sistema endocrino Un sistema del cuerpo compuesto de glándulas sin conductos que secretan sustancias químicas llamadas hormonas en la sangre.

Epididymis A highly coiled structure located on the back side of each testis.

Epidídimo Una estructura en forma de madeja u ovillo ubicada detrás de cada testículo.

Episiotomy An incision made from the vagina toward the anus to enlarge the opening for delivery of a baby.

Episiotomía Una incisión hecha desde la vagina hacia el ano para agrandar el orificio vaginal durante el parto de un bebé.

Erection When the penis becomes upright and firm.

Erección El pene se eleva y se endurece.

F

Fallopian tubes Tubes on each side of the uterus that connect the uterus to the region of the ovaries.

Trompas de Falopio Los tubos a ambos lados del útero que conectan el útero a la región de los ovarios.

Fertility awareness methods (FAMs) Methods of contraception that involve determining the fertile days of the female's menstrual cycle and avoiding intercourse during those days.

Métodos anticonceptivos de abstinencia en días fértiles Métodos anticonceptivos que implican la determinación de los días fértiles en el ciclo menstrual de la mujer para no tener relaciones sexuales durante esos días.

Fertilization The union of a single sperm and an ovum.

Fertilización La unión de un espermatozoide con un óvulo.

Fetal alcohol syndrome (FAS) A condition of physical, mental, and behavioral abnormalities that can result when a pregnant female drinks alcohol.

Síndrome de alcoholismo fetal (SAF) Anormalidades físicas, mentales y de comportamiento que pueden ocurrir cuando una mujer embarazada toma alcohol.

Fetus A developing baby from the end of the eighth week after fertilization until birth.

Feto Un bebé en desarrollo, desde el fin de la octava semana después de fertilización hasta el nacimiento.

G

Genes Units of heredity that determine which traits, or characteristics, offspring inherit from their parents.

Genes Unidades de herencia que determinan qué rasgos o características los hijos heredan de los padres.

Genetic counseling A process in which the genetic histories of prospective parents are studied to determine the presence of certain hereditary diseases.

Asesoría genética Proceso en el que se estudian las historias genéticas de los que quieren ser padres para determinar la presencia de ciertas enfermedades hereditarias.

Genital herpes An STD caused by the herpes simplex virus. Herpes simplex 1 usually causes cold sores in or near the mouth.

Herpes genital Enfermedad de transmisión sexual causada por el virus del herpes simple. Normalmente, el herpes simple 1 produce llagas frías en la boca o cerca de esta.

Genital warts Soft, moist, pink or red swellings that appear on the genitals and are caused by the human papillomavirus.

Verrugas genitales Hinchazones blandas, rosadas o rojas e húmedas que aparecen en los órganos genitales. Son el resultado del virus del papiloma humano.

English

Goal Something you aim for that takes planning and work.

Gonorrhea An STD caused by bacteria that live in warm, moist areas of the body, such as mucous membranes.

Grief counselor A professional who is trained to help people deal with the issues of sickness, dying, and death.

Hepatitis B (HBV) A viral STD that attacks the liver and can cause extreme illness and death.

Heredity Genetic characteristics passed from parent to child.

Heterosexual Someone who is sexually attracted to people of the opposite gender.

Homosexual Someone who is sexually attracted to people of the same gender.

Hormones Chemical substances produced in glands, which regulate the activities of different body cells and organs.

Human immunodeficiency virus (HIV) A virus that attacks the immune system.

Human papillomavirus (HPV) A virus that causes genital warts and warts on other parts of the body.

Incest Sexual contact between family members who cannot marry by law.

Intersexual An individual who was born with both male and female characteristics.

Intimacy A closeness between two people that develops over time.

Kaposi's sarcoma (KS) A kind of cancer that develops in connective tissues.

Labor The process by which contractions gradually push the baby out of the uterus and into the vagina to be born.

Lymphocytes Specialized white blood cells made in bone marrow that provide the body with immunity.

Español

Meta Algo que quieres alcanzar que requiere planificación y trabajo.

Gonorrea Una enfermedad de transmisión sexual causada por bacterias que viven en las zonas cálidas y húmedas del cuerpo, por ejemplo las membranas mucosas.

Consejero del duelo Profesional que ayuda a la gente con los asuntos de la enfermedad y la muerte.

Hepatitis B Enfermedad viral de transmisión sexual que ataca el hígado y puede causar otras enfermedades graves o la muerte.

Herencia Características genéticas transmitidas de padres a hijos.

Heterosexual Alguien que siente atracción sexual por personas del sexo opuesto.

Homosexual Alguien que siente atracción sexual por personas del mismo sexo.

Hormonas Sustancias químicas que se producen en las glándulas y regulan la actividad de distintas células y órganos del cuerpo.

Virus de la inmunodeficiencia humana (VIH) Un virus que ataca el sistema inmune.

Virus del papiloma humano (VPH) Virus que causa verrugas genitales y verrugas en otras partes del cuerpo.

Incesto Contacto sexual entre miembros de una familia que no pueden casarse por ley.

Intersexual Una persona que nació con características tanto masculinas como femeninas.

Intimidad Un sentimiento de cercanía entre dos personas que se desarrolla a lo largo del tiempo.

Sarcoma de Kaposi (SK) Tipo de cáncer que se desarrolla en el tejido conectivo.

Trabajo de parto El proceso por el cual contracciones gradualmente empujan el bebé fuera del útero hacia la vagina para nacer.

Linfocitos Glóbulos blancos especializados que se producen en la médula ósea y proporcionan inmunidades al cuerpo.

GLOSSARY/GLOSARIO

English

Español

M

Masturbation Touching one's own genitals for sexual pleasure.

Masturbación Tocarse los propios órganos genitales para obtener placer sexual.

Menstruation The process of shedding the uterine lining.

Menstruación El proceso de desprendimiento del revestimiento del útero.

O

Obstetrician A doctor who specializes in the care of a pregnant female and her developing fetus, and who is present at the birth of the baby.

Obstetra Médico especialista en el cuidado de la mujer embarazada y el feto en desarrollo y que está presente durante el nacimiento del bebé.

Oral contraceptives Hormone pills that, taken correctly, create changes in the female body that prevent pregnancy.

Anticonceptivos orales Pastillas de hormonas que, cuando se toman correctamente, hacen cambios en el cuerpo de una mujer que impiden el embarazo.

Ovaries The two female sex glands, which produce mature ova and female hormones.

Ovarios Las dos glándulas sexuales femeninas que producen óvulos maduros y las hormonas sexuales femeninas.

Ovulation The process of releasing one mature ovum each month into a fallopian tube.

Ovulación La liberación de un óvulo maduro cada mes en una trompa de Falopio.

P

Parenting Providing care, support, and love in a way that leads to a child's total development.

Crianza Proveer cuidado, apoyo y amor de tal manera que conduzca al desarrollo total de un niño.

Peer pressure The influence that people your own age may have on you.

Presión de los compañeros La influencia que tus contemporáneos pueden tener sobre ti.

Pelvic inflammatory disease (PID) A painful infection of the uterus, fallopian tubes, and/or ovaries.

Enfermedad inflamatoria pélvica (EIP) Una infección dolorosa del útero, de las trompas de Falopio y/o de los ovarios.

Penis A tubelike organ that functions in both sexual reproduction and the elimination of urine.

Pene Un órgano tubular que funciona en la reproducción sexual y la eliminación de la orina.

Pituitary gland The gland that controls much of the endocrine system. It releases hormones that affect the brain, glands, skin, bones, muscles, and reproductive organs.

Glándula pituitaria La glándula que controla gran parte del sistema endocrino. Secreta otras hormonas que afectan el cerebro, otras glándulas, la piel, los huesos, los músculos y los órganos reproductores.

Placenta A structure that forms along the lining of the uterus as the embryo implants. It provides nutrients to the fetus.

Placenta Una estructura que se forma a lo largo del revestimiento del útero al implantarse el embrión.

Pneumocystis carinii pneumonia (PCP) A fungal infection that causes a form of pneumonia.

Neumonía por pneumocystis carinii (NPC) Una infección de hongos que causa un forma de neumonía.

Prenatal Occurring or existing before birth.

Prenatal Que ocurre o existe antes del nacimiento.

Puberty The period of growth from physical childhood to physical adulthood, when a person develops certain traits of his or her own gender.

Pubertad El período de crecimiento entre la infancia y la edad adulta desde el punto de vista físico cuando una persona desarrolla ciertas características de su propio género.

Pubic lice Tiny parasitic insects, also known as crabs, that infest the genital area of humans.

Ladillas Pequeñitos insectos parasíticos que infestan el vello púbico de personas.

Q

Questioning Individual who questions his or her gender identity or sexual orientation.

cuestionamiento Persona que duda de su o su identidad de género u orientación sexual.

English

Español

R

Rape Any form of sexual intercourse that takes place against a person's will.

Rapid test Used in situations where the person might not come back to learn the results to the test.

Refusal skills Communication strategies that can help you say no when you are urged to take part in behaviors that are unsafe or unhealthful, or that go against your values.

Rubella A contagious disease caused by a virus that does not cause serious complications except in pregnancy.

Violación Cualquier tipo de relación sexual que ocurre contra la voluntad de la persona.

Prueba rápida Prueba que se realiza cuando la persona infectada podría no regresar para conocer los resultados.

Habilidades de negación Estrategias de comunicación que ayudan a decir no cuando te presionan a participar en actividades peligrosas, no saludables o que van en contra de tus valores.

Rubéola Enfermedad contagiosa causada por un virus que no tiene gran trascendencia, menos durante el embarazo.

R

Scabies An infestation of the skin with microscopic mites called Sarcoptes scabiei.

Scrotum A loose sac of skin that extends outside the body and contains the testes.

Self-concept The mental image you have about yourself. It is your unique set of perceptions, ideas, and attitudes about yourself.

Semen A mixture of sperm and glandular secretions.

Sexual abuse Any sexual contact that is physically or emotionally forced on a person against his or her will.

Sexual harassment Unwelcome sexual contact.

Sexuality The part of your personality that involves your sexual feelings, thoughts, attractions, and behaviors towards yourself and other people.

Sexually transmitted diseases (STDs) Infections that spread from person to person through sexual contact.

Sexually transmitted infections (STIs) Infections spread from person to person through sexual contact.

Single-parent family A family that consists of only one parent and one or more children.

Sperm The male reproductive cells.

Spermicide A chemical that kills sperm.

Stereotype An idea or image held about a group of people that represents a prejudiced attitude, oversimplified opinion, or uninformed judgment.

Syphilis An STD caused by the bacterium Treponema pallidum; it progresses in stages.

Sarna Afección de la piel causada por insectos aradores muy pequeños que se llaman Sarcoptes scabiei.

Escroto Un saco suelto de piel externo al cuerpo que contiene los testículos.

Auto-concepto La imagen mental que tienes de ti mismo. Es tu conjunto único de percepciones, ideas y actitudes sobre ti mismo.

Semen La mezcla de esperma y fluidos de las glándulas.

Abuso sexual Cualquier contacto sexual, física o emocional- mente, forzado contra la voluntad de una persona.

Acoso sexual Contacto sexual no deseado.

Sexualidad Todo lo que se refiere a ti como hombre o mujer. Incluye la forma en que actúas, tu personalidad y tus sen- timientos respecto de ti mismo por ser hombre o mujer.

Enfermedades de transmisión sexual (ETS) Infecciones que se transmiten de persona en persona a través del contacto sexual.

Infecciones de transmisión sexual Infecciones que se transmiten a través del contacto sexual entre dos personas.

Familias de un solo padre Una familia compuesta por un sólo padre y uno o más niños.

Esperma Las células reproductoras masculinas.

Espermicida Un producto químico que mata a las espermas.

Estereotipo Una idea o imagen acerca de un grupo de personas que representa una actitud prejuiciosa, una opinión simplista o un juicio sin fundamento.

Sífilis Enfermedad de transmisión sexual causada por la bacteria llamada Treponema pallidum. La enfermedad progresa en etapas.

GLOSSARY/GLOSARIO

English

Español

T

Testes The male sex glands, which produce sperm and manufacture testosterone.

Testículos Las glándulas sexuales masculinas que producen esperma y testosterona.

Testosterone The male sex hormone produced by the testes.

Testosterona La hormona sexual masculina producida por los testículos.

Transgender An individual whose gender identity differs from others of their gender.

Transgénero Un individuo cuya identidad de género difiere de otros de su género

Trichomoniasis A type of vaginitis caused by the parasite *Trichomonas vaginalis*. It affects both females and males.

Tricomoniasis Un tipo de vaginitis causada por el parásito llamado Trichomonas vaginalis. Afecta a mujeres y a hombres.

Tubal ligation A sterilization procedure for females in which the fallopian tubes are cut and tied or clamped to prevent sperm from reaching the ova.

Ligadura de trompas Procedimiento de esterilización para mujeres en que las trompas de Falopio se cortan y se atan o cierran para impedir que el espermatozoide llegue a los óvulos.

U

Ultrasound A test that produces an image on a screen by reflecting sound waves off the body's inner structures.

Ultrasonido (ecografía) Un examen que produce una imagen en una pantalla al reflejar las ondas de sonido que chocan contra las estructuras internas del cuerpo.

Umbilical cord A ropelike structure that connects the embryo and the mother's placenta.

Cordón umbilical Una estructura como una cuerda que conecta el embrión con la placenta de la madre.

Uterus A hollow, muscular organ that receives, holds, and nourishes the fertilized ovum during pregnancy.

Útero Un órgano hueco y muy musculoso que recibe, mantiene y nutre el óvulo fecundado durante el embarazo.

V

Vagina An elastic, muscle-lined tube that extends from the uterus to outside the body and is also called the birth canal.

Vagina Una vía tubular, elástica y muscular que se extiende desde el útero hasta afuera del cuerpo. También se llama el canal de parto.

Vaginitis An inflammation of the vagina caused by various organisms.

Vaginitis Una inflamación de la vagina causada por varios organismos.

Values The beliefs and standards of conduct that are important to a person.

Valores Creencias y normas de conducta que son importantes para una persona.

Vas deferens A long tube that connects each epididymis with the urethra.

Conductos deferentes Un tubo largo que conecta el epidídimo con la uretra.

Vasectomy A sterilization procedure for males in which each vas deferens is cut and sealed.

Vasectomía Un procedimiento de esterilización para hombres en que los conductos deferentes se cortan y se cierran.

Vulva External female reproductive organs. They consist of the mons pubis, labia majora (outer lips), labia minora (inner lips), vaginal opening, and clitoris.

Vulva Los órganos externos del sistema reproductor femenino. Consisten en el monte de Venus, los labios mayores y los labios menores, el orificio vaginal y el clítoris.

English

Español

Withdrawal The male's removal of the penis from the vagina before ejaculation.

Coito interrupto La extracción del pene por el hombre de la vagina antes de la eyaculación.

Zygote A fertilized ovum.

Cigoto (zigoto) Un óvulo fertilizado